PRAISE FOR
The Little Boy That Could

"…a story of overcoming incredible obstacles and defying the odds that will encourage and inspire any reader."
—Zig Ziglar, Author & Motivational Speaker

"We especially appreciated [Darren's] honest grappling with his worth apart from a pragmatic emphasis on productivity or worldly achievement…"
—The Writer's Edge

"The story of Darren Jones and his family is proof once again that when God's love is involved, statistics are meaningless."
—Vally Sharpe, M.A., Author

Tom and Joyce Jones
with Jean Vandevenne

Doctors shook their heads gravely
over our scrawny newborn...

The Little
Boy That Could
When Doctors Said He Couldn't

"Just put him in a home and forget about him,"
they advised.

praise
WORKS
- PUBLISHING -

The Little Boy That Could
When Doctors Said He Couldn't

PraiseWorks Publishing
An imprint of United Writers Press, Inc.
1-866-857-4678

www.TheLittleBoyThatCouldBook.com

ISBN-13: 978-0-9760824-3-9
ISBN: 0-9760824-3-8

Printed in the United States of America.

Cover photo: Ed Vaughn Photography, Springfield, MO
Cover design: Michael Eaton, Springfield, MO

Acknowledgments

Praise God for those with the heart
to give of themselves:

• Thank God for Jean Vandevenne, a devout Christian who was able to transform our story into a writing style that communicates spiritual ideals and values that will touch reader's hearts. She was a devoted Christian giving many long hard hours of work for the Lord. We are blessed to have had Jean, her skills, her talent and her dedication to help us tell the story of our handicapped son's life.

• Thank God for these devoted professionals and their work on the book covers:
>Ed and Judy Vaughn for their support and talent
>in generating the cover photograph and layout.
>Michael Eaton for his ideas and graphic concepts
>for the cover design.

• Thank God for Elizabeth Hamilton, author and publisher of the Character-in-Action series and a Christian with experience in foreign missions and a writing ministry. Thank you, Elizabeth, for sharing your experience in the many details—and for your spirit and knowledge that kept the project moving forward.

• Thank God for Shirley Marshall and her editing and wordsmithing skills. Having her put the final touch on the manuscript was a real blessing.

• Thank God for Darren and his siblings Andrea, Maria and Aaron who continue to love and support each other...we love you more each day!

Contents

Contents

Preface

This book is about searching outside the box for success when your child seems less than what you hope for and touches on these important points...

- One word from a child will explain what life is all about
- All problems have a purpose
- Communicating with love...not just intellect
- Calming hyperactivity without drugs
- Being successful with an I.Q. of 60
- Adaptation...no training wheels needed
- Learning and accepting what God wants for your child
- All souls and spirits are made whole...not defective
- The positive effects of nutrition on physical and mental health
- Being an advocate for your child...searching for answers
- Letting your child educate your family...
  - In love when you don't feel loving
  - In patience when you have none
  - In joy through the tears
  - In peace amidst the turbulence
  - In forgiveness when guilt persists
  - In kindness when facing insensitivity
  - In hope in the midst of despair
- Confronting self esteem...a legend trapped in your own mind
- Understanding food sensitivities and behavior
- Knowing the blessings of adoption
- Trusting in God...not yourself
- Learning why we are here...answering the question 'What good am I?'

Disclaimer

Some names of people and places, as well as some details have been changed to protect the innocent...and the guilty.

This book is not intended to be construed as medical advice. It was written solely for informational and educational purposes. Please consult with a qualified medical or health professional if you wish to pursue any of the ideas presented herein.

While nurturing our retarded infant and toddler son, keeping a diary about his condition and our feelings became a therapy in itself. Writing helped us cope with the daily hurdles we faced and was an instrumental guide as we structured our approach to life in those most difficult of times. As he continued to grow, so did our distress and the problems he encountered, and we realized that we needed to expand our resources and search outside the box to meet the ever-increasing difficulties.

We were often alone in our search. Since many of the doctors and professionals we consulted were unable to help or support us, we found that relationships with others who worked with or had handicapped children were a helpful source of vital information—and much needed comfort. This networking with other parents and teachers is an invaluable key to a child's development, and it is our desire to share this knowledge with others.

Although many factors were involved, the primary thrust of our learning experiences and our book is that all problems have a purpose. Our son was born mentally challenged and legally blind for God's Glory (John 9:3). We can now truly see the great blessing our son is—not only to ourselves, but to others as well. We praise God for this wonderful blessing and want to tell the world about it!

Tom and Joyce Jones

CHAPTER 1

Just Forget Him

The nurse folded the blanket back from the bundle she held in her arms to give us a better view of our newborn son. What a funny little bit of humanity he was! His tiny head boasted a mass of dark fuzz that arched over his eyes and came to a point in the middle of his low forehead, making him look ever so much like a baby monkey. He certainly wouldn't win the prize for being the prettiest baby in the nursery, but that didn't matter. He was *our baby!*

"Look what big hands he has!" Tom said.

"And big feet," the nurse added with a smile, further unbundling our baby to reveal feet that, like his hands, looked as though they had been attached to his scrawny toothpick limbs by mistake. "He's going to be a big boy with hands and feet like those," she said as she placed my baby in my waiting arms and walked briskly from the room.

"Weighing only five pounds and fourteen ounces, he's got a lot of growing to do," I mused, wondering why he was so tiny since he was a full term baby. Our first born Andrea, who was now two-and-a-half years old, had weighed nearly eight pounds when she was born.

Cuddling my new baby close, I leaned back contentedly against the bed pillows.

Darren Thomas Jones. The name we had chosen even before Andrea was born had a good sound now that we had someone to attach it to. Though both of us had declared that it didn't really matter whether the baby was a boy or a girl as long as it was "all right", now that our son had arrived we were glad to have a boy. One of each was ideal.

Too excited to sleep well that night, I found myself wide-awake early the next morning. Sounds of activity at the nurses" station down the hall indicated that the maternity floor was already gaining momentum for the new day. From the direction of the nursery came cries of discontent and I wondered if *our* son was among the complainers. I was contemplating strolling down to the nursery to find out when a doctor I'd never met appeared at my door.

"Mrs. Jones?" he asked, looking questioningly at me, then at my still dozing roommate and back to me again.

"I"m Joyce Jones," I said.

The doctor stepped to my bedside and gave an expert yank to the curtain between our beds to close it. Something about the way he pulled that curtain closed set off a battalion of silent alarms in my head. My thoughts immediately went to our precious little baby, and as a feeling of mild panic started to blossom inside me, I wondered if something was wrong with him.

Then this doctor, who had not even had the courtesy to introduce himself or politely inquire about my well-being, started the oddest conversation with me. I was able to recognize the fact that he was talking to me about the size of a baby's head—listing off various measurements indifferently—and for just a moment I had the surreal feeling that I was discussing cabbages with another shopper at the produce counter in the supermarket.

When he next asked me if "small heads" run in mine or my husband's family, I was still unclear as to where this was going. I thought it was a rather odd question, but told him, "No, not as far as I know."

Then, with no gentle warning or softening of his clinical tone — or any other type of kind preparation that you would expect to receive prior to someone's approaching a difficult and delicate subject — this person who is *supposed* to be in the business of *caring* for people bluntly made a statement that cut me like a knife. "Well then, something is definitely wrong because your baby's head is very small." And having apparently finished with his "cabbage business," my visitor abruptly turned and walked back out.

Instantly words like microcephalic, brain damage and retardation shot into my mind and echoed nightmarishly in my head.

I sank back against my pillows in shock, my whole world suddenly turned upside down.

I knew — far better than the average person — what having a brain damaged child could mean. Though my college degree was in Family Consumer Sciences — specializing in foods and business — the year before Andrea was born I had worked as a teacher in a school for brain damaged children. So I had experienced first hand the agonizing results of such a handicap...Our newborn son might never be able to use his hands to play ball or build things in his daddy's workshop. His feet might never run...or even walk. He might not *ever* be able to do or learn...*anything*. Although he might physically grow up, if his mental capacity never developed he faced an empty, hopeless future — that of a helpless infant locked away in a man's body.

Numbly, I reached with trembling hands for my bedside table phone to call home, while the wrenching feeling of my heart — threatening to shatter into a million pieces — flooded my mind and body.

My mother had come to help Tom with Andrea during my hospital stay, and it was she that picked up and said hello. She instinctively knew that something was terribly wrong the moment she heard my voice and quickly but gently told me that she would let Tom know that he was needed at the hospital immediately.

Although our house was only a block away, it seemed like an eternity passed as I huddled under the bedcovers and shook uncontrollably as I waited for him to arrive. At the sight of him, the sharp contrast of relief mixed with renewed pain overwhelmed me and the tears that had been paralyzed with terror streamed down my face in little rivers as I sobbed brokenly and haltingly told Tom the terrible news. For the next few days, we were thrust onto a roller coaster of emotions that wildly propelled us through a frightening succession of highs and lows.

We tried to rally following the initial, painful shock and made a valiant attempt to cling to the hope that perhaps we over-reacted and the situation was not as terrible as we had originally thought. But uncertainty slowly crept over us, eroding our hopes…after all, this doctor *was* supposed to be an expert. Then we started to plunge into a feeling of utter hopelessness. It occurred to us that maybe it was even *worse* than we thought. There might be other, more serious problems we hadn't been told about—or ones that even the doctors did not yet know!

As we fluctuated between despair and hope and then down into deeper despair, those bright, springtime mid-April days that had started out with such hope and promise were gradually forgotten, obscured by the thick black cloud of pain, anguish and uncertainty that became a suffocating prison for us as the days passed and further medical consultations left us with less and less hope for our little Darren.

It all seemed so impossible—the circumference of his head was only a scant three centimeters less than the lowest range of normal. How could such a small difference be an indication of abnormality? One of the specialists who had been called in to examine Darren gave us a chart that indicated with solid, broken and dotted lines the normal rates of growth. Our microcephalic child would not progress along these lines, he warned us dispassionately.

But how could *every one* of these doctors be delivering all these conclusive diagnoses so soon? Didn't doctors usually avoid absolute statements until they were positive about a prognosis? Especially when you consider the fact that when we asked what could possibly have caused this—the doctors said they couldn't be sure. Then how could they be so sure of our little boy's future?

Even though I'd had the flu when I was about five months pregnant—and that particular strain *was* known to cause retardation in some cases—the doctors doubted that it had been the culprit in this case. Darren's particular problems, they felt, pointed more toward toxoplasmosis, an infection caused by improperly cooked meat and parasites in cat feces. The latter was the most probable, contracted from Andrea's sandbox, though I usually kept it covered because I had been aware of this danger.

The most important question was what could be done about it? Surely, in this age of advanced technology, there was *some* cure.

But the specialists repeatedly insisted that there was no treatment available at the present time. None whatsoever. As the baby's parents, the decision was up to us, but their advice was that we seriously consider putting him in an institution: "Just put him in a home and forget about him" was the conclusion we heard over and over again. They all agreed that it was most likely that he would never be able to sit up by himself or take notice of his toys. In addition to what the first doctor had said, they reported extensive eye damage. Therefore our baby was probably blind—or nearly so—in addition to everything else.

Once the initial shock wave started ebbing, we began to just listen numbly to each new, negative pronouncement. It became almost as though they were talking about someone else's child. How could such a dreadful thing be happening to *us?* And why? Was it punishment for something we had done? Was there some lesson we needed to be taught? We didn't know!

Nevertheless, Darren was *our child* and we had *no* intention of putting him into some home and forgetting about him!

Then came the professional consensus that it would be of no use to even *try* to let our baby nurse. "*These babies*" were never able to, we were assured unanimously.

This one jarred me right out of my numbness. "Not even try!?" I objected indignantly. Ridiculous!! I insisted that he be allowed a chance to try, at the very least.

Reluctantly they gave in and Darren was brought to me.

To my delight, he quickly settled down to get his fill as though he were an old hand at nursing!

The accompanying nurse watched in amazement. "It's very unusual for "*these babies*" to nurse at all!" she exclaimed, echoing the sentiments of the doctors, "but he sure knows what he's doing!"

It may have been only one small triumph—but it felt HUGE to me! "*If only everything else the doctors have said will prove to be as wrong as their prediction about my baby's nursing!*" I silently prayed. How desperately I still wanted to believe that it was all a terrible mistake, that the smallness of Darren's head meant nothing. But deep down, I knew better...

And what about his frail little body? Would he even survive? Or would he become one of the twelve percent of "these babies" that the doctors said never even leave the hospital nursery alive?

With that thought, I plummeted into a nightmare of conflict. Maybe it would be better...though I didn't dare so much as mention it to Tom. But...*would* it be better if the baby...didn't...live?

Part of me said, "*Yes, it would be better for my little Darren to die than to have to live out his life handicapped, possibly severely.*"

But the other part of me couldn't let him go. This baby, Darren Thomas Jones, was our own flesh and blood. I loved him and I wanted him, no matter what. And maybe something could be done after all. Maybe he wasn't as damaged as the doctors thought. He had nursed like a pro—when all of the experts had been positive that it wasn't even worth attempting!

My conflict and worry increased. My first thoughts upon waking each morning were of my little baby in the nursery. Had he made it through the night? And even if he had…would today be the day that he died?

The moment of truth came the third evening of my hospital stay. At baby-feeding time, the nurses started scurrying past my door, delivering other hungry little bundles to their mothers. They had even already brought my roommate's baby to her…but where was Darren? Time seemed to drag by and still they hadn't brought him. Each time a nurse went past my door I became a little more panicky.

Just when I thought I couldn't take the suspense any longer, Darren arrived in the arms of an apologetic nurse. She explained that the delay in his arrival was because they were behind schedule due to a shortage of help that evening.

She probably wondered at the tears that were streaming down my cheeks as I took my baby in my arms and held him close. Suddenly I *knew* that what might be "better" didn't matter! *I wanted this little one to live!*

* * * * *

Although Tom was trying his best to bolster my spirits and keep me from worrying, I knew those first days were very difficult for him as well. A few days before I expected to go to the hospital, I had baked some special cookies for him to take to work to celebrate the arrival of the new baby when the time came. But how could there be a celebration now, when we didn't know from one day to the next what might happen? Tom couldn't bring himself to even appear at work for those first three days. And those special cookies remained in the freezer long after Darren and I had come home from the hospital.

In stark contrast to Darren's frail smallness, one of the babies in the nursery weighed *fourteen* pounds. He was promptly nicknamed "Moose" and the bassinets of the two babies somehow ended up being side by side. Probably someone had thought it amusing to emphasize the difference between the smallest and largest babies in the nursery and couldn't resist. But instead of discouraging us, this gave us even more hope because you couldn't help noticing that what the Jones baby lacked in size he made up for in activity and alertness — while "Moose" did nothing but just lie there! Gradually, more and more anomalies like this were cropping up and it was just so confusing. Each time, what we saw and what we had been told by the specialists were complete opposites!

At that time — back in the dark ages of the seventies — obstetricians had an almost unbreakable rule that a new mother and baby must remain hospitalized for five days. It was believed that the mother needed the rest. But I had had all the rest I could stand. I needed to get away from the depressing atmosphere of the hospital with all these doctors and specialists and their dire prognoses. And I was definitely *very* tired of all their references to *"these babies."* I wanted to get on with our life...whatever might lie ahead.

I succeeded in convincing my doctor that "under the circumstances" it would be better for all concerned if I went home early. So provided with a supply of tranquilizers which my doctor felt would be essential for my wellbeing — and which I planned to immediately flush down the toilet as soon as I arrived home — my son Darren and I were discharged from the hospital.

A kindly, elderly little nurse escorted us from the hospital to our car.

"Don't worry. He"ll be fine," she said kindly, handing Darren, who was wrapped in a fluffy blue and white blanket, to me in the car. "He's just got a lot of growing to do," she continued reassuringly.

I blinked back the tears suddenly filling my eyes—happy tears of gratitude for this small crumb of encouragement—one of the *very* few we had been given since little Darren's birth!

CHAPTER 2

Not Even Hope

Home back then was a roomy, tired old house—partially remodeled into a duplex—that we had bought soon after we were married. We had spent the better part of our spare time for the past five years remodeling it. Tom, an architect and engineer, also had skills in carpentry, plumbing and electrical wiring that he had gained while working as a teenager with his father, a carpenter and superintendent of construction. And I had learned how to use a paintbrush, refinish woodwork, remove and apply wallpaper and the like in my parents" home as well.

When we bought the house, we planned to spend about a year on the renovation. The trouble was there was never enough time and energy and—oh, yes— money!—to do all of the things that needed to be done. We also discovered early on that there was more to be done than had first met the eye.

So the work had dragged on and on and was still a frustratingly long way from being finished. To be sure, the work we had done gave promise of a lovely home someday, but there was still all too much evidence of the toll that years of neglect can inflict upon a house. My mother and Andrea were waiting at the door when the three of us arrived from the hospital. No doubt they'd been watching for us.

Wide-eyed, Andrea solemnly studied her baby brother as I sat on the sofa and unbundled him from his blanket.

"Will he...break?" she asked tentatively.

We assured her that he wouldn't, though we could understand why she asked. He was so tiny that he looked somewhat "breakable" to us, too.

Tom had her sit beside me on the sofa and then put our new baby into her waiting arms.

"Dolly!" she whispered shyly, her eyes shining.

When Tom took the baby back a few minutes later, Andrea immediately wriggled off the sofa and darted out of the room. Next we heard some thumping coming from her bedroom and then she reappeared in the doorway dragging the little doll cradle that Grandpa Jones had made for her.

"The baby can sleep here!" she announced proudly.

So with the help of Grandma, the cradle was made ready and I laid him in it. It was the perfect size for our tiny baby and during his first weeks he spent a great deal of time in it, much to Andrea's delight. She sat down softly on the floor beside the cradle, gently rocking it and chattering to the baby, who was surprisingly quieted by his big sister's tender ministrations.

I settled back into the comfort of my sofa with a big sigh of relief, glad to be back in my own home...be it ever so humble!

When friends started dropping by to welcome our new arrival, we felt the need to somehow give both our friends and ourselves the freedom to acknowledge his "uniqueness"...to a point. So we would gently tease about the doubtfulness of him winning the prize for being the prettiest baby in the nursery, while still trying to give the impression that we wouldn't want anyone else to make jokes about his appearance. At this early stage we were not ready to bluntly admit—to those close to us...or even each other—that our baby had problems...big problems.

Right from the start, it was obvious that I was going to be kept very busy trying to satisfy the needs and demands of this tiny bundle of humanity I had brought home from the hospital. Without doubt, he was a fussy baby. Frequently he seemed to be in some kind of unknowable distress. Sometimes feeding him helped, but more often, I was at my wit's end as to what to do for him. My mother stayed for a week to help with whatever needed doing and then I was on my own.

When it came time for his two week checkup with our pediatrician, I was determined to wheedle at least a few suggestions out of him as to what we could do for Darren's problems. I was hoping to see Dr. Olivetti, the doctor that was my favorite. He never seemed rushed and always took a personal interest in his patients. His associates Drs. Brown and Sanders, on the other hand, made me feel like just another problem to be dealt with and dismissed as quickly as possible. It was strictly potluck as to which one I got to see at any given time and only rarely did I draw Dr. Olivetti. My luck was evidently at a very low ebb on this day, as I found myself confronting my *least* favorite of all, Dr. Sanders.

Grunting uncommunicatively, he checked the baby and when I mentioned Darren's almost constant fussiness, he grudgingly suggested that I try supplementing breastfeeding with formula.

With that, I sensed that he was finished with us. But I wasn't finished with him.

"Doctor, I'm wondering if you can give us some suggestions for things we might try that will help his...his other problems," I began lamely.

With one hand already on the doorknob, Dr. Sanders glanced at Darren's chart — to refresh his memory as to my name, I suspected.

"Joyce," he began, in the slow, pseudo-patient tone that one might use to inform a two year old for the fortieth time that she could not have the moon as her plaything, "we *tried* to make it clear to you and your husband while you were still in the hospital that there is simply *nothing* that *can* be done for "*these babies.*" Of course you are welcome to try anything you wish, but I must reiterate that you would only be wasting your time and money."

"But he doesn't seem so different from our first baby at this stage, except for being fussy," I objected.

"Perhaps not yet. In fact, for a short while he may even *seem* to make some progress, albeit slowly, but you may be sure that eventually it *will* all come to a halt. Don't get your hopes up. You"ll only set yourselves up for disappointment. That's just the way it is with "*these babies.*"

And that, according to Dr. Sanders, was that. He excused himself and briskly walked out.

Alone in the examination room, tears streamed down my cheeks as I dressed Darren and wrapped him up in his blanket. The immense sorrow and hopelessness of the picture that Dr. Sanders had just painted continued to swell inside me until I was unable to stifle the sobs that were welling up from deep within me. Life had hit rock bottom! *Nothing* could be done! What lay ahead for this fragile little life that had been put into our hands except tragedy?

Half blinded by my tears, I made my way out of the doctors' office. But on the way home, once out of that depressing atmosphere, I started regaining my strength and resolve.

By the time I got home, my despair had turned into anger and indignation. I simply could *not* accept what the doctor had said! I *would* not accept it! Surely *something* could be done!

Not knowing where else to turn, I decided to begin with what I knew…nutrition.

That very afternoon I went up to the attic and dug out my college textbooks and all my notes. While Andrea napped and Darren remained relatively content in the little doll cradle nearby as long as I gave it an occasional nudge with my foot, I began my search.

I felt the most urgent problem was my baby's eyes. If there was anything to be done, surely the sooner the treatment was begun the better, to prevent further damage or deterioration.

I knew vitamin A was beneficial for some eye disorders and in my reading that afternoon, I was reminded that vitamin E—also a liquid in capsule form—although not necessarily associated with benefiting the eyes, offered many other important contributions to sturdy health. I determined what dosages would be safe for a small baby and then called Tom at work to ask him to stop at the health food store on the way home to pick up the vitamins.

From that day on, little golden football capsules of vitamin A and E were pierced and squeezed into Darren's mouth. He fussed, obviously not appreciating my efforts, but *I* felt much better. At least I was *finally doing something!*

"I feel like it's just us against the whole world," I said to Tom as we discussed the matter that night.

"Then so be it, I guess," Tom said with a shrug. "Darren's our kid, after all. We have to do what *we* think is best—doctors or no doctors."

* * * * *

All of Darren's clothes, new or hand-me-down, were too large for him and only added to his waif-like appearance. I could find absolutely no bonnet that would do at all. Then one day a package from my brother's wife arrived in the mail containing a tiny, white, hand knit bonnet that fit just right! It was so small that it also perfectly fit a *teacup*! I had a feeling it might and just couldn't resist trying it!

I had been weighing Darren and measuring his head every day. It became an obsession, especially the head-measuring, but I didn't care. I needed something tangible to prove, if only to myself, that he *was* making some progress…and I needed it often.

And he *was* making progress! At two months old, he had *doubled* his birth weight! And his head, though still smaller than normal, *was* growing — contrary to what the specialists had predicted — now falling just below the normal curve on the chart we had been given. Besides that, he was beginning to coo and play with his hands just as any normal two month old baby would.

About the same time, Darren developed a cough and a stuffy nose, so I took him to the offices of Sanders, Olivetti and Brown. This time, he was whisked off by himself to another room while I sat helplessly in the waiting room, listening to his screams of protest and trying to make conversation with another mother who was holding an obviously handicapped child.

The woman poured out all her difficulties and frustrations, ending with the tragedy that had befallen her family because of their handicapped child. Financial problems and stress caused by the unusual needs of the child had finally caused her marriage to end in divorce.

"Oh, that wouldn't happen to us!" I blurted out, immediately wishing I hadn't.

"That's what I thought, too," the woman said sadly.

My heart ached for her, but I also felt a little stab of fear. *What might lie ahead for our family?*

I was at last called into the inner sanctum to talk with the doctor, who to my great disappointment, turned out to be Dr. Sanders again. He gave me a prescription for Darren and asked without any real interest about his progress, so naturally he was unimpressed when I tried to tell him and rudely mumbled something about parents of *"these babies"* seeing only what they wanted to see.

Therefore, I was very surprised when he suggested that we might find it beneficial to take Darren for a complete medical and neurological workup at the

University Hospital. Without hesitation I asked the doctor to make the arrangements.

A wave of optimism washed over me. Surely a team of experts at the prestigious University Hospital would be able to help us, give us hope, offer us a sense of direction and provide us with some actual tools and ideas we could put into motion to start helping our little boy grow and develop!

So very early on a bright morning in late June, Tom and I left Andrea with a friend and eagerly embarked on the three hour drive to University Hospital—full of promise and expectation.

For the better part of the day, Darren was passed from one specialist to another, being poked and prodded and tested by each one along the way. We trailed along patiently, from one waiting room to another, quietly enduring his little expressions of displeasure and discomfort at such treatment.

"Interesting case...," each new doctor would pronounce while nodding gravely.

At the end of this wearisome tour, we were once again given possession of our "interesting case", who was by now quite tired and getting cranky. But the worst thing was that, after being put through that whole ordeal, we had not been given even *one* word of hope. The University specialists had concurred *unanimously* with those back home, repeating the same heartbreaking words—"There is absolutely nothing that can be done for a child like this. Your baby will never be anything but a vegetable. Don't bother to waste your time and money chasing after false hopes." And when we again pointed out the progress that we had seen with our own eyes, they passed it off as wishful thinking on our part. They actually believed we were just *imagining* it!

Dejected, we left the hospital in complete despair. The drive home seemed to take much longer than the trip there because all we could think about now was the time, expense and stress we had wasted on this trip, along with all of the dreams and expectations — that *at last* we would find the help we so desperately needed. We were leaving with nothing. Not even a tiny ray of hope.

But as we kept driving, questions and thoughts persisted and would not let us accept this depressing outcome. What of the progress that we had seen in our baby? We *knew* that it was *not* merely wishful thinking! Even at only three months, Darren was definitely *not* a vegetable. Just because some specialists could not see — refused to acknowledge — the progress he had made, we, as Darren's parents, could *not* accept *their* prognoses and just ignore or deny what we had *observed with our own eyes!*

So when we asked ourselves if we should just give up, the answer was an emphatic NO! Instead, we made a solemn pact on that drive home that *on our own* we would do everything in our power to nurture our sweet little baby who was now sleeping, exhausted, in the back seat. We would *search* for answers — and we would *find* them! Anything promising that wouldn't harm Darren, we would try! By the time we pulled into our driveway, our resolve was firm and we were determined to help Darren...and what those specialists, Dr. Sanders and all the other doctors had said no longer mattered to us!

CHAPTER 3

The Survivor

My stepfather passed away the week after our trip to University Hospital. It was a very sad time for all of us. My own father had died when I was in my late teens and now Andrea and Darren would not have the opportunity to know and love this grandfather either.

Predictably, our already hectic life became even more hectic. After the funeral came the formidable task of helping my mother close their home in Florida. Until she got her bearings and decided what she wanted to do, we wanted her to move in with us. Since Tom had no vacation time available, it was left entirely up to me to engineer and execute the entire process.

So on a hot mid-July day, my mother, Andrea, three month old Darren and I set off on the two day drive south.

About an hour from home Andrea got sick all over the back seat, and Darren was even fussier than usual the entire trip there. It was not a pleasant drive.

The situation did not improve during the time we spent at our destination either. Besides the agony of deciding what to keep and what to get rid of, it took a garage sale that lasted *five days* for us to sell all of the expendable items. The stifling job of packing the U-Haul trailer in the heat of a Florida summer was bad enough, but to make matters even worse, we had to do it *twice* — as well as *un*load once — because the first trailer didn't quite hold everything. Then there was the first-time experience of driving with a trailer behind the car on the way home and having to be ever-mindful not to get caught in a situation where we would have to *back up* with that trailer. I had *no* idea how to accomplish that successfully...and all of this was being done with an active, curious toddler and an ever-hungry, ailing infant needing almost constant attention!

The whole expedition ended up being one long nightmare and the experience left me absolutely drained. But it did lead me to the realization that, having lived through it all, I could survive anything. This turned out to be a very good thing because Darren's first year — the time we would always look back on as the "Year of the Bad Guys" — had only just begun.

* * * * *

The first thing I did when we arrived home was take Darren to the pediatrician. Fortunately, we saw good old Dr. Olivetti who discovered that Darren had an ear infection. It turned out to be the first of six infections he suffered — all prior to his first birthday.

After giving Darren a shot, Dr. Olivetti turned his attention to me. He could see that the emotional and physical stress I'd been under was affecting my spirit. Gently, he told me "It's like raising 10 normal children." He then scribbled something on his prescription pad, tore off the sheet, folded it and pressed it into my hand as we left the office.

Oddly enough, the doctor had written down the chapter and verse of a Psalm. But, unfortunately, because of his typical physician's scrawl, I couldn't decipher two of the numbers. Curious, but hesitant to call a busy doctor just to tell him I couldn't read his handwriting, I looked through the Psalms in my Bible, checking every possible combination of what I hoped the numbers might be, but none of those verses really fit my situation.

During my search, though, I did stumble across the first verse of Psalm 46: "God is our refuge and strength, a very present help in trouble." I wondered if this was the message Dr. Olivetti was trying to convey since the passage seemed so meaningful to me—I certainly was in need of a refuge, strength *and* help. The only problem was that I had no idea how to *find* them.

I decided to print out that inspiring verse and put it on our refrigerator—with a yellow happy face magnet holding it in place—for two reasons...first, to provide me with the reassurance that help *was* out there whenever I felt despair, or had to yet again hear that dreadful phrase that was repeated to us over and over again by each new group of doctors or specialists in that detached, fatalistic tone—"*these babies*". Plus it would also give me the strength to continue my search for that help—no matter how long it took or how difficult or elusive it was to find!

CHAPTER 4

The Year of the Bad Guys

During Darren's first year, he came down with one cold after another, and nearly every one was accompanied by an ear infection, which in turn called for a trip to the doctor and a round of antibiotics. If it wasn't ear or respiratory problems, it was diarrhea. Frequently recurring rashes that were pesky, painful and irritating further added to his discomfort. So it was really not surprising—and certainly understandable—that he was a fussy baby.

The constant care he required as a result of all this was beginning to take its toll on me, but it hurt me when my mother suggested that perhaps I was spoiling him. "Just let him cry sometimes," she added. It seemed to me I *already* did that quite frequently when I ran out of other options.

Over time, it had become evident that Darren enjoyed being where the action was, so I'd started keeping him nearby, even when I was working around the house. One Saturday in September he was reclining in his baby seat on the kitchen counter while I was fixing lunch and heating his bottle in a pan on the stove. I stepped to the sink for just a moment and as I was turning back to the stove, I heard a loud clatter and then saw the pan of hot water—along with the bottle and Darren—fly into the air. Somehow he had fallen out of his baby seat!

I caught him midair, but not before the boiling water had scalded his head and upper body. I immediately held him under cold running water in the kitchen sink, simultaneously calling frantically to Tom, who was working in the basement.

He bounded upstairs and we quickly bundled up our screaming baby, picked up his bewildered sister since my mom was out shopping at the time, piled into our car and raced to the hospital.

In tense silence, we waited in the hall while the rapidly assembled burn team went to work in the emergency room. As young as she was, Andrea somehow sensed the seriousness of the situation and sat quietly between us. Every now and then, she would look up at first one of us and then the other, wide-eyed, as if trying to understand what was happening. All we could do was reassure her with a silent pat and a warm hug.

At last a doctor came out and gravely informed us of the extent of Darren's burns. With carefully selected phrases, he confirmed our worst fears as he explained the extent of the injuries.

There were third degree burns on Darren's left shoulder and head — including his left eye and ear — although it was too soon to tell whether this would affect his sight or hearing. Also, there was possible damage to his scalp, which may result in hair loss. He said that had it not been for the immediate application of cold water [I silently thanked God for my first aid training!] the damage would have been much more severe and extensive. Even so, he cautioned us, the outlook was guarded — sometimes babies with burns this severe do not make it.

In anguish, we followed the cart as they wheeled the still form of our baby to the isolation ward. He was now connected to an unsettling array of bottles and tubes — his head almost unrecognizable because of the heavy bandages covering it. Then Tom left to take Andrea home while I stayed with Darren.

A turbaned, masked and white-gowned nurse efficiently introduced me to the infection prevention procedures of the isolation ward. After being properly disinfected, turbaned, gowned and masked myself, I was led into a little white room with a view of the sterile white crib that held my small child. It soon began to feel like a prison cell as my overwhelming guilt about what had happened threatened to slowly suffocate me.

In my mind a nightmarish surreal courtroom scene was playing out in which no one was in charge so witnesses and prosecutors were free to scream hurtful accusations at me while I sat there helpless to defend myself because of my own deep guilt.

There was no denying that it was an accident, but I was also tormented by the realization that down deep I still wondered if it would be better for Darren to die than to live out his life handicapped by mental retardation.

I thought I had settled this question that evening back in the maternity ward when the nurses were late in bringing him to me and I thought he had died. The joy and relief that he was still alive were real then, but in the months since that incident, the doubts would occasionally return. Sometimes when I'd hit a real low, I had even toyed with the idea that a mother who *truly* loved her child would not allow him to suffer such a life. I had even gone so far as to wonder how...

The fact that I could entertain such ideas shocked me abruptly out of this train of thought and I tried to console myself that it was Darren's happiness and well being that I was concerned about.

But was it? Or was it because I didn't want to be saddled for the rest of my life with the heartache, expense, work and responsibility of a handicapped child? Did I want to be rid of him? Was *that* the reason I had been so careless as to leave him too close to the pan of boiling water? In view of the evidence, how could I deny my guilt?

Tom returned to the hospital as soon as my mother had gotten back home and could watch Andrea. Once he had been given instructions and sterile-wear, he joined me in the tiny white cell.

As we kept vigil that evening at the hospital, I couldn't help blurting out over and over again, "It's all my fault!"

Each time I did this, Tom would doggedly insist "Oh, Joyce, it wasn't *your* fault!"

After about the tenth time he added, "…but how in the world *did* he make contact with that pan of boiling water?"

Through my tears I dejectedly mumbled, "I guess he just saw the pretty shiny pan and wanted to touch it." But after dwelling on that for a moment, I was hit with an exciting realization…he had **not** been *that* close and he'd been *lying* in his seat which was in a *reclined* position! He would have *had* to do more than simply reach out with his hand…

"Tom!" I exclaimed with joy. "He would have **had** to …to…*sit up! All by himself!!*"

We looked at each other in growing awe and wonder. Somehow our child, who had been sentenced by the entirety of the medical profession to living out his life lying helpless and immobile on his back, *had propelled himself forward!* It was the *only* possible, logical explanation of what could have happened.

"I guess no one ever bothered to explain to Darren that a vegetable just lies there oblivious to its environment — with no interaction whatsoever," Tom said dryly.

I was greatly comforted by this revelation that I had *not* been negligent or acting irresponsibly after all. According to my knowledge and expectations of Darren, I *had* placed him at a safe distance from the stove. How could I have known that he was capable of raising himself up and forward enough to reach that pan of boiling water?

And at only five months old, very few "normal" babies could even do that!

Later that night, as I lay tossing and turning, both mentally and physically, on a hospital cot trying to nap, I again wrestled with the dilemma of what would be "better" for him. Although I didn't consider myself a particularly religious or spiritual person, in other crises, I had found solace in prayer. Now, though, I didn't know what to pray for. At least it didn't seem proper to me, in my ignorance of the ways of God, to lay before Him my deep, dark thoughts that it might be better for our child to die than to live severely mentally handicapped. You can't pray, "Dear God, please let my baby die," can you? Or could you?

As night turned into morning, I drifted in and out of sleep. Then abruptly I reached a turning point. I found myself praying with urgency, "God, *please* let him live! Let my baby live! *No matter what!*"

Darren and I ended up spending ten seemingly interminable days in the hospital. Every day there was the agony — for Darren — of having the deteriorating skin stripped from the burn sites so new skin could grow and — for me — of waiting outside the door listening to his screams of pain during each of these ordeals.

Then there were the long hours spent in that white prison cell, with little within its sterile limitations to keep a five month old infant and his mother entertained and content.

Surprisingly though, in spite of his suffering, Darren was less fussy than usual. This was probably because I was constantly at his side when he was awake and, as I also did at home, I talked to him — chattering about whatever came to mind. And then, when I ran out of ideas I recited nursery rhymes and poems. Sometimes, when I was sure no one was around, I would sing to him. Poems and songs I wasn't aware I knew came pouring out. How wonderful is the human brain to be able to store such things away unnoticed and effortlessly retrieve them years later?!

Darren, looking like a caricature out of the Arabian Nights tales with his head still heavily bandaged turban style, lay there solemnly taking it all in, sometimes responding with cooing, arm waving and kicking.

Dr. Johnson, the specialist in charge of Darren's case, was not a local man, but "happened" (by the Mercies of God) to be in the city, having been called in to oversee another patient. Dr. Olivetti confided that he was the best burn man in the country, and we were fortunate that he was nearby.

On Darren's third day in the hospital, both doctors stopped by and Dr. Olivetti introduced the renowned doctor—a tall, good-looking man of indeterminate age from the east coast.

Dr. Johnson spoke to Darren playfully for a moment, then divided his attention between Darren and his chart, mumbling to himself and occasionally scribbling something on the chart. At one point he snorted, shook his head and exclaimed, "This child's eyes are too bright for him to be retarded!"

Finally, snapping the metal cover of his chart shut, he happily informed me that he felt our baby was making excellent progress. There seemed to be no permanent damage to either his sight or his hearing. Perhaps there might be some hair loss, but probably not. There may also be some scarring, but a little plastic surgery would take care of that. We would have to wait and see.

My eyes filled with tears of joy as relief flooded through me while I watched him walk out the door. Darren was going to be all right! Thanks be to God! Then the doctor's amazing pronouncement "this child's eyes are too bright for him to be retarded!" hit me. I immediately called Tom at work—a practice in which I seldom indulged—to tell him what the doctor—a *doctor!*—had said about Darren! We happily reveled in the bright cheer that Dr. Johnson had left behind.

* * * * *

Darren awoke from his afternoon nap on the first Sunday after he was released from the hospital and I brought him into the living room to join the rest of the family.

"Darren!" Andrea called from the floor amid a collection of dolls, books and pillows. She patted a space in front of one of the pillows, inviting him to join her.

I stooped to lay him with his head and shoulders on the pillow. But Darren didn't lie down. He *sat!*

"Look, everyone!" I exclaimed. He sat there for a moment, a bit wobbly and swaying from side to side until I eased him back against the pillow.

In view of our conclusions that first evening in the isolation ward as to the cause of Darren's accident, we shouldn't have been surprised at this newest feat. However, our joy was in no way diminished. We all clapped and exclaimed with such gusto that poor little Darren began to whimper in confusion.

Tom swept him up off the floor in a big bear hug. "I don't think I'd feel any more pleased if my kid had just won an Olympic gold medal!" he said with emotion.

* * * * *

I started to religiously apply good old vitamin E oil to Darren's burns, as well as continuing to give it to him orally. The doctor was amazed at how quickly the scars were disappearing when he examined Darren a few weeks after the accident, but he didn't seem to want to take into consideration my home remedy. No matter. I continued the treatment and eventually Darren was left with only one small scar on his shoulder.

On the doctors" advice, we made another trek to University Hospital. Naturally, we went a bit reluctantly, remembering the bitter experience we had last time, though now that Darren was sitting up by himself, we *were* a bit curious as to just what the specialists would say about his progress *this* time.

But per the usual, no one had any interest in a demonstration of Darren's achievements until it was late in the day. First, tests must be done for the records. By the time all that business was taken care of, Darren was thoroughly fed up. He was in no mood to show off for anyone — and certainly not *these* tormentors — so he stubbornly flung himself backward every time an attempt was made to have him sit up.

The doctors did have to admit that he had made some progress, but they *still* did not think it likely that he would continue to do so. It seemed that the whole of the University Hospital staff was allied in a conspiracy to try to convince us once and for all to give up on our handicapped baby. *Why?* We wondered. *What was wrong with giving parents a little hope? Wasn't it part of the doctors' job to be encouraging, optimistic and as positive as possible?*

Though Darren was progressing quite well in spite of what the doctors had predicted, he certainly could not be described as a robust child. He was definitely a picky eater and milk was the only food he would take with consistent enjoyment. I was constantly on the lookout for something to tempt his finicky little appetite.

One day as I was having lunch, he showed a keen interest in my peanut butter sandwich!

Hmmmmm, peanut butter for a baby? I wondered. *Well, why not? Peanut butter was nourishing. It didn't require a mouthful of teeth to chew it. Maybe it would help to fatten him up.* So I gave him a taste. He immediately gobbled it down and wanted more. So peanut butter was added to Darren's menu.

About that time, the bouts with diarrhea began. Like the ear infections, they would come and go, but mostly they came. The doctor would put him on the classic diarrhea diet of cottage cheese, Jell-O® and 7-Up®. Just when I would think the problem was licked, there it was again.

Giving up on the doctor's treatment, I did a little research on my own and learned, first of all, that this diet could actually cause the problem by bringing about a deficiency in vitamin B. I discussed my discovery with Dr. Brown, the doctor for that day. He agreed that the diet *could* do that, but he offered no other alternative. He seemed to think this was something we would have to live with for the time being.

But all the while Darren was suffering and getting thinner and thinner...and Dr. Brown didn't have to change dirty diapers all day. Something had to be done and it suddenly occurred to me that I would probably have to be the one to do it. It would be nice if the doctors had all the answers, but if they did, they weren't talking. It was beginning to seem like I was going to be on my own more and more when it came to finding answers for Darren.

On the assumption that some food was causing the problem—and then I wondered why I hadn't thought of that before—I started a diary that kept track of both what Darren ate and recurrences of the diarrhea. After weeks of record keeping, I concluded that peanut butter was the culprit.

Later on, I realized that what actually triggered the diarrhea was probably a combination of peanut butter and the antibiotics that Darren had been given to battle his frequent ear infections. Acidophilus should have been given along with the antibiotics to balance the natural flora that antibiotics kill along with the bad bacteria. But this hadn't occurred to me yet.

CHAPTER 5

Hanging on to Hope

Just after Thanksgiving, my mother moved back to Florida to escape the approaching northern winter. It had been good to have her here these rugged months and we would miss her.

Christmas came and went with about as little to-do as we had ever experienced since we got married. We put up a tree and bought and wrapped the necessary gifts, but I had neither the time nor the energy this year to do all the little extra holiday things like baking and making special gifts and decorations that I had so enjoyed in past years. It was just not the usual joyous Christmas season.

We were invited to Tom's family's Christmas celebration that year, a drive of 150 miles, but Darren came down with a bad cold and ear infection two days before Christmas, so the four of us spent a quiet Christmas day at home.

* * * * *

Back in the days when I worked at the school for brain damaged children, I had heard of a therapy called *patterning* — that although not universally accepted by the medical profession, sometimes worked wonders for brain damaged children. I had read an article on the subject, but remembered only that it consisted of an intensive program of special exercises that paralleled the movements that normal babies make as they learn to move about crawling, creeping and walking. I wondered if this sort of training might be beneficial to Darren, although his development so far had honestly been quite close to normal.

On hands and knees, I worked with him on the living room floor, painstakingly moving first one arm, then the opposite leg, in an attempt to teach him how to crawl. He was delighted to have Mommy down at his level, but our sessions didn't seem to be accomplishing anything else. I decided I needed help, but...where to find it?

After some sleuthing in the phone book and a few calls, I hit pay dirt. Mona McCormack, a therapist with a social services agency, showed up on our doorstep one snowy afternoon just after lunch. She spent half the afternoon explaining the theories behind her program and demonstrating her techniques on Darren.

Though the system was somewhat different from the patterning I had read about, I was impressed with Mona's knowledge—and by the time she left I was excited about the possibilities this therapy might present for Darren. I felt a kind of camaraderie with Mona that I suddenly realized had been missing in my life since Darren's birth. I hadn't had time to do much socializing and the few friends I ran into casually seemed to shy away from talking about him. Here at long last was somebody who understood his problems and was willing to discuss them with me. On top of that, she was a professional with a program that offered some real hope—something to do that might actually turn the tide for our handicapped child.

Mona came once a week and on the other days I faithfully followed the program she set up. Her coming, as to the exact time, was undependable and sometimes she would appear just moments after Darren had fallen asleep. Because of his delicate health, I felt he needed all the sleep he could get, so I hesitated to wake him on these occasions. Instead, I would persuade Mona to show me any new therapy so I could carry it out myself.

Unfortunately, that turned out to be a mistake on my part. Mona phoned one day to say that she wouldn't be coming any more. She said there were others who needed her services more than Darren did, now that *I* had the program down pat.

I was devastated. Yes, I *could* and I *would* continue the exercises with him. But *I* needed Mona. I needed a friend. Obviously, Mona hadn't known what her support had meant to *me*. It was demoralizing for me to realize that I had been only another name on Mona's list of people who needed help.

Whether because of or in spite of the exercises, Darren went through the acceptable phases of crawling, creeping and, finally, shakily, standing on his own two feet to walk holding onto a firm support!

* * * * *

The end of his first year was marked by yet another trip to University Hospital. Had it not been that this time he was also scheduled for consultations with specialists regarding his ear infections, we probably would *not* have gone this third time — since our past visits had been so fruitless and discouraging. What it boiled down to was a kind of feud we were carrying on with the experts at the hospital, though it wasn't likely the experts themselves were aware of it.

We wanted them to acknowledge that there *was* something that could be done for "*these babies*." The exercises, the special effort we had put into providing a stimulating environment, the love and attention, the nutrition program...we felt they were all paying off. Here was a brain-damaged child who was developing and progressing at an almost normal rate! Surely that proved *something*, didn't it?

But no, not to the specialists at University Hospital. This time they could not ignore or explain away as a figment of his parents" imagination that this tiny brain damaged child was actually *walking* — not quite by himself — but doing very nicely by holding on to a steady hand. Yet *still* they clung to their same old conservative, hope-killing train of thought. There was a suggestion that perhaps they had erred "a bit" in their earlier prognoses. However, it surely was not likely that there would be much *additional* progress. They wouldn't want to raise any false hopes, you understand!

We were alone in an examination room when a young doctor, probably an intern, with the inevitable clipboard and stethoscope appeared. He asked questions and chatted cheerily to Darren as he checked his reflexes and measured just about everything about him that was measurable.

"Good enough!" he said as he took one last measurement of the circumference of Darren's head.

Then, turning to us on his way out the door, he said matter-of-factly, "You know, about one percent of microcephalic youngsters do develop more or less normally."

Dumbfounded, we stared at the doctor's departing back and then at each other. He didn't *say*, "and this child seems to be doing just that" but he left us with that distinct impression! In any case, he was still the *first* doctor we'd spoken with since Darren was born that had actually admitted that even *ONE* child such as ours had developed normally!!

"Do you think angels ever appear in doctor's garb?" I asked Tom. This doctor's cheery optimism was such a change from the discouraging words we had come to expect from the University Hospital staff that we had the feeling that we had had a visitation from Above.

"Hardly ever," Tom said in a hushed voice. "Like, maybe, once in a lifetime."

As to the ear infections, the ear, nose and throat men concurred with the pediatricians back home that the insertion of tubes would certainly be worth trying.

So, Darren began his second summer with a brief and uneventful visit to the local hospital to have this minor surgery. Happily, the procedure worked and that was the last of the ear infections.

The day after his surgery, Darren seemed to be slightly under the weather, but the pediatrician—Dr. Olivetti thankfully—could find nothing wrong.

Then, the day following Dr. Olivetti's examination, Darren broke out in a rash. I called the doctor's office. Dr. Olivetti was out of town and Dr. Sanders took the call. He confirmed my fears. No doubt, Darren had the measles!

We worried. How much more could this little guy stand? And what might measles do to his already damaged eyes?

The next day Saturday, Dr. Olivetti phoned. He had learned that Darren had the measles and he was concerned, not so much for the baby, as for the baby's *mother*! He feared that the measles, on top of everything else was just too much and had called to offer whatever support and reassurance he could. Dear Dr. Olivetti! Knowing that he had been concerned and was trying to help gave me a lift just as the Bible verse he'd shared with me had.

As it turned out, the measles was among the lesser of the bad guys that had been on Darren's trail since his birth. It was a light case and when it was over, there appeared to be no further damage to his eyes.

CHAPTER 6

The Dark Cloud Lifts

Darren's second summer passed quite uneventfully. We hadn't had a genuine crisis for weeks. Maybe we were at last coming out from under that dark cloud that had been hanging so close overhead ever since his birth.

The Wednesday after Labor Day, Andrea's preschool, good old Hunny Pot, opened its doors for the fall term. Andrea, in the back seat of the car with Darren, bounced with anticipation as I drove across town for the first session of the year.

Hunny Pot, with its Winnie the Pooh theme, was a veritable wonderland for a young child. Situated in a rambling old mansion, each room was furnished for a different activity — music, art, nature study, crafts, reading or math. Being a student at Hunny Pot was a happy learning experience. Andrea looked forward to every session and talked incessantly about what went on there both during and between sessions.

I knew both Betty Fletcher and Dianne Morris, the women who ran Hunny Pot. Betty and I had worked together quite closely at the school for brain-damaged children where I taught before Andrea was born. Now as we pulled up under the carriage porch connected to the mansion's wide veranda, Betty came running out to say hello. In the course of the conversation, Betty asked if we had considered enrolling Darren in preschool.

Flabbergasted, I could only stare at her for a moment. Then, knowing Betty as well I did, I said, "You're not kidding, are you?"

Betty shook her head. "Oh, no. Dianne and I talked about it when we came to Andrea's name as we went over this year's enrollment."

"But he's not even potty trained, or...or...anything!" I objected.

"I know, I know," Betty said, "and we"ve never had any handicapped children. No one's ever asked us. But we'd really like to try, if you're interested. It would be good for the kids we already have and it could be a good experience for Darren—normalization and all that, remember?"

Normalization. Yes, I remembered. Normalization was the prime concern of Vince Kern, the guiding light of the school where we had taught. What it all boils down to is helping a handicapped person lead as normal a life as possible in as normal a setting as possible. We were convinced of the validity of the principle and worked continually to see that it was put into practice for Darren. We would expose Darren to the same activities and the same people that a "normal" child would experience. We would search for and promote his normal niche in life. But preschool for one so young?

Betty also reminded me of another important principle—early and prolonged intervention—and we were certainly working on that.

"Think about it!" were Betty's parting words.

I promised that I would, deeply touched by Betty and Diane's interest in Darren.

Tom and I discussed the matter that evening. We had long ago decided that we would try anything within reason that wouldn't hurt Darren, and Hunny Pot certainly seemed to fit into that category quite nicely...

So...at the ripe old age of seventeen months, Darren began his school career. The following Monday at 9 AM, I delivered him along with Andrea to Hunny Pot. He clung to me as Betty greeted them on the veranda.

"Now promise me that if you see this isn't going to work out, you"ll tell me," I said. "I'll understand." At this point, I was almost hoping it wouldn't work out. I was having second thoughts about leaving our little handicapped child even in the capable hands of Betty and Diane.

"He"ll be fine," Betty assured me, taking Darren's hand. He looked back at me tearfully as he was led inside and I drove home feeling like a cruel fairy tale mother abandoning her child to the unknown terrors of the forest.

I had planned to spend the morning shopping and running errands unencumbered by children. Instead, I decided to go home to be near the telephone — just in case "things" weren't working out for Darren. I put in a load of laundry, then busied myself scraping wallpaper off our dining room walls, a job that had been abandoned since before Darren's arrival.

Somehow I resisted the urge to phone Hunny Pot just to see how Darren was doing, but I was there right at the stroke of twelve, which was dismissal time.

I spotted him in the far corner of the playroom in the company of an enormous stuffed Winnie the Pooh. He looked sleepy but contented. Betty and Diane assured me that there hadn't been any problems. He didn't do much but watch, but he seemed to enjoy himself.

There were no tearful partings after that first day — an indication, we hoped — that we had made the right decision. Hunny Pot on Monday, Wednesday and Friday mornings quickly became a comfortable part of Darren's schedule. We felt good about it for him.

I felt good about Hunny Pot for myself, too. Much as I hated to admit it at first, I came to relish those six hours a week that permitted me to back off from the burden I had been carrying since Darren's birth. It felt good to know that somebody else was involved in our struggle to help Darren overcome his handicaps.

* * * * *

Having a little time to work on the house again had lifted my spirits. I hadn't realized how depressing chipped paint and peeling wallpaper can be until I got back to work on the dining room. Actually, the only room in the house that we could call "done" was the living room. At least we did have a decent place to entertain guests. As summer eased into fall, things were looking up. Even the weather seemed to be in tune. I sat on the back steps one beautiful Indian summer morning in late October enjoying a cup of coffee and scanning the morning paper. It was a non-school day and Andrea was giving the Raggedy Ann and Andy dolls my mother had made for Andrea and Darren last Christmas a ride up and down the sidewalk in her little red wagon. Darren sat in the sandbox banging a beach pail with a little shovel. I was about to think of some other activity to divert him from the nerve-jangling one he was presently involved in when an ad announcing the Annual Downtown Halloween Parade caught my eye.

We hadn't gone last year because Darren had one of his many ear infections, but there was no reason why we couldn't go this year.

Then *The Great Idea* struck me! Why not make costumes and let the kids walk for a little way in the parade, just for fun. And, as Andrea came stumping up the sidewalk with the Raggedys in the wagon, I knew just what I'd make for costumes. Surely, between my collection of cast-offs and some boxes my mother had left behind, I could find what I needed for Raggedy Ann and Andy outfits. Andrea could pull Darren in the wagon and they'd each carry their Raggedy doll!

When my poor husband arrived home that evening, the house was a mess and dinner wasn't ready...but the matter of costumes for the Halloween Parade was well in hand!

Halloween turned out to be another balmy Indian Summer day. I fed the kids early and dressed them in their costumes, noting with satisfaction how well the red yarn wig with the white sailor hat perched on top I'd made for Darren concealed the size and shape of his head. For once he could actually be described as cute.

After a quick supper, as soon as Tom got home from work, we gathered together all our Raggedys and their little red wagon and drove downtown.

As they had been in past years, the sidewalks were lined with people waiting to watch the parade. Tom let the Raggedys and I out of the car at the beginning of the parade route.

"Meet you in front of the courthouse," he called as he drove off to find a parking place.

I was glad to see that we had arrived just as the parade was getting underway. I knew Darren wouldn't be patient for very long if we had to wait around for it to start.

I settled Darren in the wagon with Raggedy Andy and gave him a sucker, hoping that would keep him content so he would sit quietly for a block or two. Andrea, holding Raggedy Ann in one hand, pulled Darren and the wagon into the parade line with the other hand.

Walking along the curb to keep an eye on the kids, I soon discovered that my costume idea was not original, to say the least. It appeared to be the year of Raggedy Ann, with beautifully costumed Anns and Andys of all sizes and shapes. But from the remarks I caught, none were as captivating as my diminutive Raggedy Ann pulling my even more diminutive Raggedy Andy in her little red wagon.

Andrea, with her short legs, had trouble keeping up with everyone else. Soon there was a sizable gap between her and the clown riding a unicycle that was in front of her, but no one seemed to care. When Andrea and Darren came into view as they rounded a curve, the crowd began to applaud. They passed on by, completely oblivious to the stir they were causing. I could scarcely contain my delight and wished Tom could have seen it! But the courthouse was still a block away.

They had just reached Courthouse Square when a photographer from the *Daily Tribune* stepped from the curb to snap the kids' picture. Then a man with a two-way radio, a clipboard and a ribbon on his lapel that said *Parade Official*, handed Andrea a card. She veered from her course to give me the card which read: "Congratulations! Your entry has been selected as a winner. Please meet us at the booth at the end of the parade route for the awarding of prizes."

A winner!?!

"Kids, you"ve won a prize!" I squealed with delight. Raggedy Ann plodded on, unimpressed, as did her brother. Neither of them really understood the meaning of winning a prize. But I did...and I was thrilled!

Now, where was Tom? I scanned the faces as we passed by the courthouse and couldn't see him anywhere. Well, they couldn't pull out of the parade now, not when they were winners! Andrea seemed to be holding up all right and Darren was doing fine in the wagon. But I thought I would burst if I couldn't share their triumph with somebody—and soon!

Tom emerged from behind the crowd as we arrived at the park. Darren wriggled his now sticky-faced little self out of the wagon, leaving Andy behind. He ran to Tom, tugging on his pant leg to be picked up. Tom obliged. Andrea promptly jumped into the wagon and with me pulling it, we went to join the huddle of excited prize winners in front of the booth.

While we waited for the end of the parade and the arrival of all the winners, I washed the sticky from Raggedy

Andy's face at a drinking fountain while he dozed on Tom's shoulder. With the help of Raggedy Ann, the dolls did a wild dance routine in the wagon while we waited.

Finally a man took charge of the microphone in the booth and began to award the prizes, a $25 savings bond for each category. I nudged Andrea to jump out of the wagon and go up to accept their prize for "Cutest Couple."

Triumphant, we made our way through the crowd still milling around the downtown area to the alley where Tom had parked our car.

Now that I had had a taste of winning, a new plan was forming in my mind as we walked back. There was a kid's costume contest at a department store on the North side of town. Why not go? The kids were still dressed up and Darren had had a little nap, so he should be in a good mood for a while.

We were held up by traffic on the way, so when we arrived at the door of the auditorium where the contest was being held, it was already in progress.

A buxom lady in a navy pant suit peered at us over her half spectacles and bellowed out, "Wait! Wait! Hold the contest! We"ve got somebody else!" She then escorted us directly to the stage where the contestants, a rather unruly mob ranging in age from toddlers to junior high school students were lined up for the judging.

The next thing we knew we were being handed a blue ribbon as cameras flashed. First Prize! But we hoped we wouldn't meet the mother of the second prize winner in a dark alley afterward because it was obvious from the thunderous look on her face that she thought *her* child — a chubby witch complete with a real live black cat and broomstick — had been destined to receive First Prize — until we walked in, that is!

We soon learned the prize was a ten speed bicycle. I summoned up the courage to ask if something else could be substituted for the ten speed since the kids were so small. It would be *years* before even Andrea could ride a ten speed.

The contest committee graciously decided that we could pick out up to one hundred dollars' worth of toys suitable for our children's ages. A hundred dollars' worth of toys! Wow!

Our new friend in the navy suit escorted us to the toy department where we spent an idyllic hour. "Take all the time you want—there's no hurry," the lady had said.

By this time the kids were understandably tired and we had a little trouble getting even Andrea to comprehend the rules of this amazing new unheard of game of picking out one hundred dollars' worth of toys.

As we roamed the aisles, however, she fell in love with a beautiful big brown teddy bear, so we took that. Darren veered off toward a display of brightly colored animal riding toys. After trying them all, he favored a green caterpillar with wiggly gold wire antennae, which we claimed for him.

Perfectly content with the one toy each had chosen, Andrea and Darren lost interest in even looking at any more toys, though we hadn't come anywhere near the hundred dollar limit yet. After a good deal of deliberation, we chose a little electric organ that we thought both kids could enjoy for a long time and several educational toys that we had been wanting to buy for them, but thought were too expensive.

There were pictures to clip in the newspaper the next morning. The account of the contest at the department store said the brother and sister team of Andrea and "Andy" Johnson had won First Place, but the pictures looked so adorable, we weren't going to be picky about names. I sent off clippings to the grandparents so they could show them off and brag about their grandchildren.

Then as we drank our morning coffee we talked about how we had put our microcephalic, "different" little boy in a parade in front of the whole town. In the rush of life, we had put his "abnormal" conditions completely out of our minds! And as different as he may actually have been, he had been totally accepted...the same as any "normal" child!

CHAPTER 7

McMuffin

The highlight of Christmas Day that year for Andrea was a little white dog that belonged to Mom and Dad Jones' next door neighbor. Grandpa took the three older grandchildren over to see her while the younger ones napped. We never saw the dog, but we heard about her *all* the way home.

Andrea informed us that her name was Muffin—well, McMuffin really—like an Egg McMuffin at McDonalds. She was soft and fluffy like a ball of cotton. She could do tricks and she was fun to play with. Some day Andrea wanted a dog *just like her*. Some day *soon*. She would save her money and buy one.

Well, Daddy wasn't so sure about that...and neither was Mommy!

But that was far from the last we heard about getting a dog. Once home, Andrea drew a picture of a shaggy white dog and asked me to write "Muffin" underneath it. Next she drew *more* pictures and labeled them herself. Then she made an entire *book* about Muffin. When she had completed it, she read it to Darren, and after that she took it to Hunny Pot for Show and Tell! By now we were beginning to realize that this was **not** a "passing fancy" that would soon evaporate and blow away!

One day she found a picture of a dog that she said looked exactly like Muffin in a library book about dogs. It was a West Highland White Terrier, the book said, often fondly called a "Westie". If the dog was as irresistible as its picture, we could understand Andrea's infatuation with the Muffin she'd met at Christmas!

I started to daydream about an adorable little shaggy white Westie named Muffin…imagining her playing with our kids…picturing her curled up on a rug by the kitchen door sleeping cozily. But wait a minute! That was ridiculous! The *last* thing our family needed was a dog. The kids were too young for a pet. And *I* certainly didn't have time to train a dog, no matter how irresistible she might be.

But apparently Tom had been infected by Andrea's "Muffin mania" too. He called home from the office one day with the phone number of a kennel somebody had told him about that bred West Highland Terriers!

"They probably cost a fortune," he said, "but why don't you call…just to satisfy our curiosity?"

So I called. They *did* cost a fortune, though not as much as we had expected. Then we were issued an invitation to come by and meet the dogs and informed that we would be most welcome any time!

That was our first mistake — going out to see them — and the second was taking Andrea and Darren along.

The kennel owner, a petite lady with shaggy white hair herself, escorted us inside an immaculate little brick building on a blustery January Saturday afternoon. We were greeted by a volley of friendly barking as shaggy white dogs of various sizes — which could best be described as animated, well groomed string mops — leapt up to meet us.

Our host reached into the cage and picked up one of the medium sized mops. "This one would be perfect for your family," she said, stroking its shaggy coat.

It was a female, six months old and housebroken, which was a pleasant but unexpected surprise. And, of course, she had "papers." Not that we cared about that. We were more interested in her manners than her family tree.

She settled down quietly in her owner's arms, her bright little eyes peering curiously at us through feathery bangs. Andrea was drawn to her like a magnet and gently stroked her. Darren put out a tentative hand when the lady stooped to his level, and having once touched her, couldn't leave her alone.

Her name was Princess—Princess McDougall, to be exact— but the lady didn't think there would be any problem if we wanted to call her something else.

"How about Muffin?" Andrea piped up immediately. How could we possibly call a West Highland Terrier anything else?

"Oh, sure!" the lady said. "Princess Muffin McDougall. How about that? Muffin for short."

She set the dog down on the cement floor. Andrea stepped backward a few steps and slapping her hands on her thighs like a pro, chirped, "Here, Muffin! Come, Muffin!"

The dog suddenly came to life and bounded over to Andrea, all aquiver with excitement and anticipation.

"She knows her name! See, she knows her name!" Andrea squealed, squatting to pat and hug the little dog. Then she jumped up and led a wild, merry chase around the room with Darren and Muffin.

"What do you think?" Tom spoke softly in my ear as we watched the blossoming love affair between our kids and the newly christened Princess Muffin McDougall.

What did I think? I thought there was *no* way we could go home *without* this adorable little creature...small fortune or not!

Andrea had already dedicated her entire bank account—the accumulation of money gifts for Christmas and birthdays for the past couple of years—to getting a dog. We decided that if Darren were old enough to understand about such things, he would be willing to make his contribution, too. So, we cleaned out the kids' savings accounts and added a little from our own and Princess Muffin McDougall was ours!

That evening the kids played with Muffin on the kitchen floor while I made pizza for supper. Watching Darren with the dog, I could understand why the experts didn't advise combining dogs and little children. He simply could not keep his hands away from her. He was particularly fascinated by her wagging tail that was constantly in motion. Then without warning, before I could stop him, he grabbed her tail as though it were a handle and picked her up!

Poor Muffin! I rescued her as quickly as I could. The little dog gratefully licked my hands, which, besides saving her from pain and indignity, were no doubt delicious because of the grease on my fingers from the sausage I'd been putting on the pizza.

It was amazing that Muffin had made no move to defend herself from Darren. Not even a growl! That was sweet little Muffin's way, we would discover. From then on she simply kept a wary eye out for that little boy with the grabby hands and became quite expert in keeping a balance between playfulness and self-preservation. She put up with handling from him that she wouldn't have tolerated from anyone else.

Several days passed before our household settled down to normal after Muffin's arrival. The kids just couldn't get enough of her and wanted to play with her constantly. She took it all in stride and when she had had enough roughhousing, she would simply disappear for a while under a bed or behind the sofa for a nice refreshing nap and a brief respite.

CHAPTER 8

The Door to Speech

Doors, doors, doors! There were five of them in our dining room: double French doors, each with *twelve* panes of glass; corner cupboards on each side of the bay window with double doors that had six panes of glass above a solid panel; and finally the solid paneled swinging door into the kitchen. At this point in our renovation project, which had dragged on all winter, that was about four doors too many for me. I had removed most of the paint from the woodwork in the room several years earlier, uncovering the fine oak underneath.

Now my task was to dig out the little lines of paint embedded in the crevices along the panes of glass and around the decorative molding.

With the coming of spring, I concentrated every spare moment I had on that dining room, determined to finish this seemingly endless project and maybe even have a dinner party to celebrate.

So when I had the bare necessities of my other work done, I would scoop up Darren, saying, "Come on, let's go work on the doors." To solve the problem of keeping him occupied and out from under foot while I worked, I had an ever-expanding collection of playthings that he was allowed to have *only* when I was working in the dining room and they were becoming his favorite toys. Therefore, he would play contentedly while I scraped paint and muttered about doors, doors, doors.

Darren had had frequent colds that second winter and had missed quite a few days of preschool. But without the ear infections of his first winter, we could easily take the colds in stride. All in all, as we watched our almost two year old toddle about the house, we had a great deal to be thankful for—he had progressed *so far* beyond what we had been led to expect.

Our greatest concern at the moment, other than his eye problems, was that he did not talk—he had not uttered one word yet, not even daddy or mommy. He seemed to understand much of what we said to him, but communication on his part was strictly via body language or crying.

One day as I was washing the breakfast dishes, Darren began tugging at my skirt and, wonder of wonders, instead of crying, he seemed to be trying to *say* something. I shook the water off my hands quickly and stooped down to his level. "What do you want, Darren?" I asked.

"Oor! Oor!" he said insistently, as though he was perfectly accustomed to using words.

I was thrilled that at last he was attempting speech, but what was he saying? I longed to be able to reward his attempt by responding appropriately.

"Show Mommy," I said.

He led me into the hall to the closed French doors of the dining room. "Oor!" he repeated, still more insistently.

Door! He wanted Mommy to work on the *doors* so he could play with his favorite toys! After all of my constant muttering about those five doors, it was no wonder that Darren's first word was *door*!

I picked him up and hugged him, tears brimming in my eyes. "Door?" I said, touching one of the doors and emphasizing the "d" sound at the beginning of the word.

"Oor," he echoed, struggling to get down and on with the business on the other side of the "oor".

"Okay," I said, "we"ll work on the doors right now!" The dishes could definitely wait.

And so the "door" to speech was finally opened for Darren. More words came slowly at first and always without the beginning sound, but they came!

* * * * *

Early that summer, we took Darren for yet another workup, this time at a hospital in an out of state university. But as usual, every time we took him for these examinations by the "professionals", we wondered afterward why we had bothered — we always left in a state of depression. This new team did at least acknowledge that he was making progress, but they didn't encourage us to expect that the progress would continue. The EENT doctor suggested that a visit to an ophthalmologist might be in order. Perhaps — just *perhaps* — there might be something that would help Darren's eye problems.

So off we went chasing rainbows yet again, taking Darren to an ophthalmologist — which was an overnight trip. After what must have been a very trying hour in the doctor's schedule- how *does* one determine just what a two year old with a vocabulary of maybe six words actually sees? — glasses were prescribed.

Glasses! How in the world were we going to keep glasses on Darren? The doctor didn't seem to think of this as his concern. Apparently it was his job to prescribe them — and ours to see that Darren wore them.

Several times we found the glasses in the grass just before the lawnmower did, but for the most part, once the glasses were on, they did stay on. The fact that they were usually slightly askew didn't seem to bother Darren in the least. But whether they actually helped or not was anyone's guess. We sure hoped they did.

Andrea was quite fascinated with the idea that her little brother wore glasses and drew a bigger-than-life-size portrait of a dark haired, freckle faced little boy with enormous black rimmed glasses and labeled it DARREN. Interestingly enough, she pictured Darren with a big head...the way we all *wished* he would look. Actually, it was a pretty good likeness, considering. So I framed it and hung it in the hall with our collection of family photos.

CHAPTER 9

Fire!
Fire!

Early in the summer, about the same time that Darren finally caught on that the word "door" had a "d" sound at the beginning, the dining room renovation was finally completed. Tom wired and installed an antique chandelier that we had bought at an auction years ago and we brought the round oak pedestal table and chairs that had belonged to Tom's parents out of the storeroom. We decided that the room looked so elegant that we simply must have a dinner party to show it off.

So, on a Saturday evening soon after that, we invited three couples we had met at church to join us for one of my favorites — a "cook-it-yourself-at-the-table" Chinese Hot Pot dinner.

Tom had been working upstairs and was heard thumping around all day both overhead and down in the basement.

Everything for the dinner was under control by the middle of the afternoon, so I was contemplating sitting down to relax for a few minutes before dressing for the evening.

Suddenly Andrea and Darren, who had been playing by the stairs in the hall came running into the kitchen.

"Mommy! Mommy! Come look!" Andrea shrieked, grabbing my hand and pulling me to the stairway.

"Ook!" Ook!" Darren echoed, pulling on my other hand.

A gray cloud of smoke was billowing down the stairs! Now it was *my* turn to shriek. "Tom! Tom! The house is on fire!"

Tom came bounding up the basement stairs. "Get me some buckets for water," he shouted and raced on up to the second floor.

Grabbing our only bucket from the kitchen closet, I dashed up the stairs with it.

Tom met me at the top of the stairs coughing and waving the smoke away from his face. "Call the fire department," he shouted, grabbed the bucket and disappeared into the cloud of smoke, still coughing.

I called, thankful for the emergency numbers sticker on the phone, then herded the kids and Muffin, who had been following close at my heels, out to the front porch and settled them on the swing with strict orders to stay there. I gave Andrea the responsibility of seeing to it that Darren and Muffin obeyed.

The swing turned out to be a ringside seat for the arrival of the bright red fire truck that came screaming down our street and halted in front of our house about two minutes later.

"Fire truck, Darren! See the fire truck?" Andrea yelled.

"Uck! Uck!" Darren yelled in turn.

Firemen swarmed out of the vehicle and into action. Three of them burst unceremoniously through the front door, donning gas masks as they thundered up the stairs and disappeared into the cloud of smoke. All the while Muffin was objecting vehemently to the invasion of her territory with sharp incessant barking. As I stood helplessly in the hall, one of the firemen reappeared, ushering Tom down the stairs.

"I"m okay!" Tom insisted, gasping and coughing. His watering eyes had caused streaks to run down on his sooty face and his hand was burned when he had grabbed a fire extinguisher that was too close to the fire.

"You get outside too, lady," the fireman said, herding us to the front steps with the same dispatch I had used with the kids and Muffin just minutes earlier. He motioned to another man, apparently a paramedic, who came over to us immediately and started applying respiratory equipment to Tom until his breathing was normal again.

By that time, the fire was out and the firemen were packing up their equipment, most of which they hadn't used. There hadn't been much of a blaze, one of them informed us. Apparently, a bathroom heater had malfunctioned and started the fire. He went on to say that we were lucky to have mostly just smoke and water damage.

Muffin was still objecting with sharp little barks as the truck pulled away from the curb. The kids were subdued and wide-eyed as we all went inside to view the damage.

Smoke still lingered on the stairway and throughout the upstairs but, as the fireman had said, we *were* lucky. It could have been so much worse.

With the windows open and a couple of fans strategically placed at the front door and an upstairs window, the smoke gradually cleared. The acrid *smell* of the smoke, however, permeated the whole house. It would take a long time to get rid of that.

We wondered if we should call off the dinner party. But what would we do with all that food? We decided that if we could stand the smoky smell so could our guests. We mopped up the water that had leaked through to the kitchen below — but fortunately *not* onto any of the food — and proceeded according to plan, including giving the kids their supper and putting them to bed. After the afternoon's excitement, it took a bit of doing to get them settled down before it was time for our guests to arrive. Darren was still mumbling, "Uck! Uck!" as he fell asleep. Well, at least he had added "truck" to his vocabulary.

"You burned the dinner!" the first arrivals guessed, sniffing the air as I greeted them at the door.

"No, I didn't!" I said. "We almost burned the house down!"

Well, as you can imagine, we certainly didn't lack for a topic of conversation to get the party under way that evening. And when it was all over, our guests rated the evening as one of the best they had ever spent...even though it would forever be associated with the pungent smell of smoke.

CHAPTER 10

On Parade

By the time Halloween rolled around again, I felt like an old hand at the business of parades. The previous outing had been a great family experience...a true family highlight that had brought us closer together. Plus I now felt at ease exposing my precious but different little guy to the world—even in a town parade. But I knew we had to have a gimmick in order to win—like Raggedy Ann and Andy with the wagon last year. Not that I really expected to win two years in a row, but it sure would be fun trying.

My inspiration this year was some colorful authentic costumes that my sister-in-law had sent us from Guatemala. But the crowning glory was Darren's mascara mustache—the only part of his costume that wasn't authentic.

He and Andrea both giggled in delight when I set him in front of the mirror to paint it on during a dress rehearsal the morning of the parade. But I was met with stubborn resistance when I tried to remove it before we went to the store. Darren put up a howl that probably could have been heard two blocks away when he realized what I was up to. However, I endured the howl and removed the mustache anyway. With the exception of a Halloween parade, I was not about to appear in public with my two and a half year old son wearing a mustache!

Tom declined to be in the parade, although he promised to cheer from the sidelines like last year. He also wanted to make a little cart for me to pull the kids in. It turned out to be a rather ambitious project for such short notice and he was busy in the basement up until the day of the parade making the cart from a wooden box and a pair of antique metal wheels that had been in the garage when we bought the house. He hastily painted it that morning with brown paint which turned out to be still tacky that evening, which meant that at the end of the parade, my hands were the same color as the cart.

The weather was not as mild as it had been the year before. In fact by late afternoon, it was downright chilly. We had put straw in the cart to make it more comfortable for the kids to ride in and it turned out to also be a nice cozy nest for them to burrow down into to keep warm.

To make a long story short, we won first place in the group division. There were no more contests to enter, so we went home that evening joyful and triumphant, clutching the $25 savings bond prize and a blue ribbon. Having won a prize in the Halloween parade contest two years in a row, there was no stopping me when the Bicentennial Celebration rolled around the next Fourth of July. Darren himself was the crowning glory this time — he and the wicker baby stroller that had been in Tom's family for over a hundred years. Admittedly, without the stroller, we might have escaped notice, cute as Darren was in his unauthentic costume. He wore a ruffled white blouse that had been Andrea's, red suspenders, some blue corduroy pants cut off at the knees and laced with shoe strings to make knickers, white knee socks, a red bow tie and a jaunty little black derby that I had worn in grade school.

Tom joined in the dressing up this time and the rest of us were decked out in what were costumes compatible with the period of the wicker stroller. Most of the articles were items we had picked up from auctions, with the exception of Tom's straw hat, a relic of his father's from the twenties.

We won over a hundred dollars worth of prizes before the day was over. First Andrea and her decorated bike won a prize in the kiddies' parade. Then in the main competition, the four of us won first place for best family group and Darren—all by himself!—took first place in the "Little Shaver" division.

By the time the judging was over that beastly hot day, Darren was cross and tired. He had never been a thumb sucker, but even though he was three now, he still liked his pacifier when he felt in need of comfort—and this was one of those times. I swallowed my pride while we were making our way out of the crowd and gave him his "old friend," which I still carried in my purse for emergencies.

While we were waiting to cross the street, a photographer from the newspaper came over and wanted to take his picture.

"Oh, just a minute, let me take his pacifier away," I said quickly.

"Don't you dare!" the photographer said, laughing. And click went the shutter.

In the next day's paper, there was Darren, pacifier and all, a perfectly fetching picture of a little shaver from long ago.

At home after the parade, I packed a picnic supper while the kids napped. Late in the afternoon we headed for Rock Park, a small, shady city park within walking distance of home. As we had hoped, the park was not crowded, even though it was a holiday. Probably most of the population had chosen one of the bigger parks with a pool. All we wanted just then was some shade and peace and quiet.

We picked a picnic table near the swings and slides and ate our supper. After we had eaten, Tom went with Andrea to push her on the "big kid" swings while I supervised Darren as he climbed on and off the down end of a teeter-totter.

As he played, minding his own business, a pretty little girl of eight or nine with long blond hair came along and stopped beside him. Looking Darren square in the face, she shouted, "You're ugly!" Then she stuck out her tongue, made a face at him and ran away.

The senseless insult made no impression on Darren, but I felt as though I had been kicked in the stomach, my emotions a turmoil of anger, fear and helplessness. Was this a glimpse of the sort of treatment my handicapped child would meet all through his life? I wanted to strike out at this rude, saucy child who had so needlessly intruded in our lives and been so hurtful. I wanted to go after her and tell her what a mean and despicable thing she had done. And I wanted to gather my dear little ugly duckling close in my arms and somehow be able to shield him forever from such painful comments.

I didn't tell Tom or anyone else about that incident in the park at the time. It hurt so much I just couldn't talk about it.

We walked home at dusk, got the kids into their pajamas and then the four of us sat on the back steps and watched the fireworks that the Chamber of Commerce sponsored every Fourth of July at the city ballpark. We were more than a mile from the park which was quite close enough for Andrea, who loved to watch the brilliant colors burst across the sky but didn't care much for the loud explosions. Even at this distance, she huddled close to me, ready to clap her hands over her ears whenever the booms came.

This was Darren's first experience with fireworks. He crawled into Tom's lap and gave a little squawk and put his hands to his ears every time there was an explosion. He wasn't much interested in the colorful display in the sky. *Could it be that he couldn't see it?* we wondered. *Or maybe it didn't look the same to him as it did to us?*

What **was** *it like in his little world?* I wondered as I sat there in the dark. *And how would I ever cope with what* *might lie ahead for him?* The fireworks booming and flashing across the sky seemed to echo the turmoil within me.

When the fireworks were over, Tom and the kids scrambled to their feet and went into the house to find a bedtime snack. I stayed on the steps in the dark feeling completely drained — physically, mentally and emotionally. And sooooo tired. Suddenly I realized that I had been tired for a long, long, time — for such a long time in fact that I had grown used to it. Keeping extremely busy had become a therapy of sorts so tiredness had become a way of life for me. Maybe I should go to the doctor for a checkup...

CHAPTER 11

The Hundred-Mile Donut

Before I could decide whether my tiredness was enough of a problem to warrant a visit to the doctor, Tom came home from work with news of a job promotion, contingent upon moving to Stanton, halfway across the state.

Of course, we had to consider what would be best for the kids. Because Andrea would be starting kindergarten in the fall, she would be making a change anyway. We could foresee no problem as far as she was concerned. But would we be able to find a preschool that would compare with Hunny Pot for Darren? Probably not. Still, he couldn't go to preschool forever. No doubt he would need to be put into special education of some sort sooner or later. Stanton was a larger city. There would possibly be more options for help there.

And if we were going to move, we would have to work hard to get the house ready to sell.

The next thing we knew, a *For Sale* sign was planted in our yard. And I was frantically keeping everything shipshape so the realtor could bring by prospective buyers, so I didn't have time to be tired just now.

Also, we had our own house hunting to do, not an easy task in a strange and distant city. We had decided that this time we were going to buy a house that didn't need remodeling. One that we could just move into without having to do anything at all.

The house we finally settled on—after several exhausting trips to Stanton—was a compromise. Although it was a relatively new house, it was in need of some redecorating, but we decided we could handle that.

Moving day was the last Saturday in August. Tom had hired a couple of sturdy college students to help load the rented moving truck the night before. Besides doing last minute packing, I was busy keeping Darren out from underfoot. He was absolutely enthralled with the truck and Tom had promised him that tomorrow he could ride in it all the way to the new house. Just him and Daddy. The problem was that Darren wanted to go *now*. Never mind all the furniture and stuff!

"Uck! Uck!" he kept insisting, getting crabbier and crabbier every time we told him he'd have to wait until tomorrow to ride in the truck.

Between all the confusion of moving and the frustration of having to wait to ride in the truck, by bedtime he was practically bouncing off the walls and so was everyone else. It took a long time to get him settled down to sleep and then he kept crying out all night long.

We were all up early, if not bright, that Saturday morning. Turning a deaf ear to Darren's continual clamoring to ride in the truck, we finished emptying the house—filling both the car and the truck to capacity.

At long last the two men of the family got into the cab of the truck and off they drove with not even a wave or a backward look from the smaller one.

Andrea and I wandered numbly through the empty house—hand in hand—with Muffin pattering behind.

"Good old house!" Andrea said in a tight little voice.

"Yes," I whispered, feeling that if I spoke aloud a dam somewhere inside me would burst open with pent up tears for all the memories this good old house harbored. Under this roof I had spent some of the happiest — and some of the most difficult — times of my life.

"What awaited us under the roof of the new house in Stanton?" I wondered as I drove off with Andrea and Muffin in the loaded station wagon to catch up with the moving truck.

We all stopped at about the halfway point of our journey for coffee, milk and donuts. Darren was still too excited about riding in the truck to want to be bothered with eating, so we let him take his donut with him.

Almost two hours later when we pulled up in front of our new home, he was still clutching that donut with not a nibble missing.

CHAPTER 12

Defective by Design

The first visitor in our new home was a chubby girl of eleven or twelve with bright blue eyes and blond hair. She told me that her name was Cathy Peterson, she lived across the street and she had come to play with our children.

"Well, come on in!" I said impulsively, even though the house was still cluttered with unpacked boxes. What was one more child underfoot?

I continued with the unpacking until it suddenly dawned on me that there weren't *any* children underfoot. I followed the sound of little voices down the hall to Andrea's room where all three of them were happily occupied — apparently playing school. I tiptoed back down the hall to continue my work. I was relieved when I realized that a parental visit at this point seemed quite unnecessary.

At noon Cathy left amid protests from both Darren and Andrea.

"Come again!" I invited, fervently this time.

"I will!" Cathy promised as she went skipping down the sidewalk.

Watching Cathy go I thought, *"What a jewel of a child!"* Although it was my first impression of her, I never did change my mind. She remained an absolute pleasure to know.

All during our settling in, Cathy—our "friendly neighborhood social director," as we came to call her—took Darren and Andrea under her wing, helped them get acquainted with the other children in the neighborhood and happily mothered Darren from that time forward.

We had long since come to the realization that Darren's hyperactivity and sometimes erratic behavior was more than most people cared to cope with. It was with profuse apologies that we left him with a hired baby sitter, and we would have to be really desperate to have the courage to ask a friend to look after him—even for a short time. But Cathy needed no apologies. She absolutely adored little children and Darren, being the youngest in the neighborhood, was her own special little child. He, in turn, adored Cathy. Though he was still his own sometimes out-of-control and ornery self, Cathy had a way with him that we envied. She was truly a godsend in our time of need.

Tom's sister, Loraine, who also lived in Stanton, dropped in one day and volunteered to take Darren to the park so I could work on my latest project—papering the upstairs bathroom. I couldn't refuse an offer like that! But before I got involved in the wallpapering project, there was another matter that I had been wanting to take care of.

The trigger for this "other matter" was an incident that happened recently. Darren had come in from playing outside and asked me if I would eat rocks.

"No, of course not," I responded. "Why do you ask?"

The reason, as it turned out, was that some of the older neighborhood boys—evidently realizing that Darren was "different"—were teasing him and told him he couldn't be their friend unless he ate some of the small rocks along the edge of the street. Darren, however, was not taken in by their perverted idea of fun. I was saddened that they would try to take advantage of him, and I determined then and there that I needed to help these boys to understand why he was different. Now was my chance.

I sent Andrea to quickly round up the neighborhood kids and bring them to the side door. In short order about fifteen of them appeared, some of whom I had never even seen.

I greeted them and explained that I wanted to thank everyone for making my family welcome in the neighborhood and especially for being such good friends to Darren.

"You've probably noticed that Darren is different from other three year olds—he doesn't talk as well as others and he can't see very well, either—and I want to tell you why." I instantly had everyone's attention as I continued. "Before Darren was born he got sick—kind of like when someone gets the flu. If that happens before a baby is born, when it is still developing, it may slow down the way its brain grows and it may even hurt its eyesight. Well, that's what happened to Darren. He couldn't help it and it wasn't his fault. It could happen to any one of us. If you got very sick or you were in a car accident, your head or your eyes could get hurt so that you might have the same problems that Darren has. Just think if that *was* you—not able to think quickly or to see very well. I think you would like to be treated the same way you are treating Darren—with kindness—and I thank you so much! I just wanted you to know the whole story."

The little audience quietly disbanded when I had finished, but from then on, there was a special bond—a family feeling—not only with Darren, but among all the children in the neighborhood.

Soon after we moved to Stanton, we decided we needed to start going to church regularly. We liked to think of ourselves as "church people," but we hadn't been regular attendants for some time now. And so our second Sunday in Stanton found us headed for church.

With considerable reservations we handed Darren over to the lady in charge of the nursery, knowing that he wouldn't sit quietly with us in church. He bellowed in protest but the lady insisted that he would be all right.

We will never forget the sermon that day. The text was the ninth chapter of the Gospel of John—the story of Jesus healing the man that was born blind.

"Who did sin, this man, or his parents, that he was born blind?" the disciples wanted to know, taking it for granted that *someone* was responsible for the man's handicap.

We knew where they were coming from because we had been there too. Why *do* bad things happen? Was every bad thing that happened punishment for someone's wrongdoing? Why had Darren been born handicapped? We had agonized over that time and again. Was it punishment for something *we* had done? And if that was so, *what* had we had done to deserve such a severe punishment?

Jesus' answer was, "Neither this man nor his parents have sinned, but that the power of God at work in him might be seen." The man's handicap would show *God's Glory!* He was defective by design...for a reason, a purpose. He was defective only in *their* minds. God knows all of us before we are born. He forms us in our mother's womb and He does not make mistakes.

The minister pointed out that the issue was *not* who was responsible for the man having been born blind. "Bad things happen," he said. "It's the kind of world we live in—a world under the bondage of darkness and sin. But that is why Jesus came: To overcome the world! No one is exempt from trouble. Godly people suffer as well as the ungodly. Jesus said to His disciples, 'In the world you shall have tribulation, but be of good cheer. I have overcome the world.' He can turn the tragedies, the bad things of our lives, into good. God purposes to show Himself in affliction, to make Himself known, to reveal what He is like: all-wise, all-powerful, completely loving."

When we went to get Darren after church, he was sitting on the floor banging his heels and throwing toys. The ladies in the nursery seemed inordinately happy to see us, which didn't surprise us.

"They seem like such nice people," we overheard one lady say as we left. From her tone, she might as well have added, "but of course, they can't be. Really nice people wouldn't have been given a child like that!"

"We *are* nice people!" Tom said to me jauntily as we went down the hall.

"Too bad she missed out on the sermon today," I commented dryly. I was glad that *we* hadn't missed it, although we were still trying to fully understand it.

We looked down at the whiny toddler pulling at my skirt, wanting to be carried, his glasses askew — the whole of him, in fact, askew and a little grubby. Our little Darren. Could we dare to hope that some day *"the works of God would be manifest in him,"* as Jesus had said of the blind man?

CHAPTER 13

New Hope

Cathy Peterson was not the only plus of our move to Stanton. In a casual conversation over the fence with our next-door neighbor, Peg Martin, I learned about Prescribed Activity Center (P.A.C.), an unusual and innovative "school" in the city. Peg volunteered as a program evaluator/developer for the center. When I walked back into the house, I was excitedly clutching a packet of information Peg had given me.

Pouring a cup of coffee, I sat down at the kitchen table to look over the material. Or maybe devour would be a more accurate description.

Founded by the parents of a Down Syndrome child, P.A.C. was described as an eclectic nonmedical treatment center for handicapped children from infancy to thirteen years. The goal of the center was to help such children achieve their learning potentials through programs individually designed around each child's neurological, behavioral, perceptual, educational and nutritional needs.

"Wow!" I thought, getting more and more excited as I continued to read. We had been having some discussions lately as to the kind of help we felt we needed for Darren. It appeared that P.A.C. offered everything we were looking for...with some extras thrown in that we hadn't even thought of!

In addition to a resounding "Wow!" that echoed mine, when Tom looked over the P.A.C. material that evening his reaction was, "Do you think it could be as good as it sounds?"

We noticed Peg was out working in her yard, so we went over and plied her with questions about P.A.C. while we helped her weed a flowerbed.

We concluded, as we went home after our talk with Peg, that about the only drawback we could see regarding P.A.C. was that it was closed right now for summer vacation. Later, when we thought about this and wondered if it "just happened" that we moved in next door to Peg, we decided not. So many times we can look back through the years and see how our Heavenly Father was working on our behalf, even when we weren't smart enough to ask Him for help. We knew in our hearts that this was just one more indication of His guidance.

Andrea started kindergarten the day after Labor Day. Darren—in his stroller—and I walked the four blocks to school with Andrea although she really didn't think she needed an escort. Looking quite fetching in a red plaid dress with a white collar and cuffs, she waved goodbye at the kindergarten door and happily marched in to begin her public school career.

Choking back the tears that welled up in my eyes as I thought about our little girl reaching another milestone in her life, I went home and called P.A.C. to make an appointment to get the wheels rolling on the next step in Darren's education. I was quite pleased to be given an appointment for that very afternoon.

Prescribed Activity Center was housed in several large rooms in the basement of a Lutheran Church. After a brief wait during which I was asked to fill out an information sheet, we were ushered into the small office of Karen Woods, the founder and director of the center. Surprisingly enough, she was neither a medical doctor nor an educator—but simply a determined, motivated parent who wanted to help handicapped children. I immediately felt at ease with her, though Darren was his usual wiggly, uneasy self in spite of the box of toys in one corner of the room.

Karen spent about a half hour explaining the program and answering my questions before taking us on a tour of the center. I was impressed with the comfortable, relaxed atmosphere as we watched the "teachers" working with the children, some obviously handicapped. The staff consisted of Karen, an assistant to help manage the program, a secretary and several devoted volunteers — one for each child — to carry out the individual programs. In addition to the staff they had an impressive list of qualified people who served P.A.C. in an advisory capacity on a volunteer basis.

There were about twenty children at P.A.C. that day. I learned that children of preschool age could attend full time, others half days or every other day — and some who were also in regular school would only attend for an hour or two per week. It was all very flexible, with programs that were adapted specifically for each child...there was even one for those who were homebound.

At the dinner table that night, learning about Andrea's first day of school had priority so Tom and I didn't have time to discuss P.A.C until the kids were in bed. Not that there was much to discuss. We had already more or less decided that it was just what Darren needed. Even though it would be expensive, my visit had confirmed our decision.

I took Darren to the center on Thursday for a half day of testing and observation and then the staff consulted on a program of activities for him. The following week he began attending P.A.C. half days on Mondays, Wednesdays and Fridays. Another big step for our little guy!

CHAPTER 14

The Experiment

The program outlined for Darren by the Prescribed Activity Center was not just limited to the time that he spent there, so his first few weeks were a time of orientation and training for me as well as him. I spent several hours at the center — plus many more at home — learning the procedures and routines, as well as the philosophy behind them.

Basically the program consisted of activities designed to enable a child to learn at his own optimum level, freeing him as much as possible by removing obstacles that were blocking his way. There was also extensive training in areas such as visual, auditory and tactile perception; motor development; self-help; language, reading, math and science; and even creativity. Each student spent his time at the center under the constant guidance of a specially trained volunteer who worked only with that one child and who saw to it that the activities were carried out exactly as prescribed. Interesting pieces of equipment to stimulate brain development were strategically placed all around the room. Equipment like Vestibular stimulation tubes to spin in; ladders hung horizontally to practice proper gripping and swinging from rung to rung to increase eye-hand coordination; tables and gymnastics mats to perform patterning exercises; and plastic bags that they would breathe into while being carefully monitored and timed which helped them to develop deep breathing habits that provide more oxygen to the brain. The center's library was extensive and included books on patterning, reading and nutrition published in the 70's and 80's. Similar contemporary books by the same authors are *How to Teach Your Baby to Read: The Gentle Revolution* by Glenn and Janet Doman and *How to Teach Your Baby Math* by Glenn Doman. And *Prevention Magazine* was and still is a veritable goldmine as a source for articles on exercise and nutrition. Some of the special learning equipment used at the center—books, games, toys and tools—was also available to supplement the program at home.

Part of Darren's daily program—both at home and at the center—was potty training, an activity that interested him not at all. In fact, he was not very much interested in any part of the program, so his volunteer teacher had to spend a great deal of time enticing him to participate in activities which it seemed to us he would have thought to be fun.

During this time Andrea seemed to be having problems with school. There had been no complaints from her teacher Mrs. Thompson as yet, but every day after school, she would go crying to her room and continue to cry for twenty to thirty minutes. When I spoke with Mrs. Thompson, she said she had noticed that Andrea seemed rather tense in the classroom, but was doing well in her work. Perhaps she needed time to adjust to the move. We put our concerns for Andrea on hold, hoping that time would take care of the matter.

As I continued to read the materials from the center, I was quickly discovering that nutrition was very important to the P.A.C. staff. I became more and more convinced that my college studies had left some large gaps when it came to my knowledge about nutrition. Now here was something else—food as related to behavior and learning problems!

One reference on the subject of how refined food affects behavior—*The Psychodietics Book* by Drs. Cheraskins and Ringdorf—was particularly convincing.

While it was admittedly a controversial subject, after our many experiences with Darren—and all the so-called experts and their opinions on what would and wouldn't work—controversy wasn't necessarily a problem for us. After all, we had long ago said that we would be willing to try anything that wouldn't harm him. Soooo...we plunged headlong into P.A.C.'s nutrition program—which met with immediate apprehension from my family—starting with Andrea.

"Green beans for breakfast? Is that what Darren gets for breakfast, Mom?" Andrea asked, standing on tiptoe beside the stove to see if I was really heating up *green beans*.

"Yes, that's what he gets for breakfast," I said, not adding that it was what he would get for lunch, dinner and snacks too—for the next four days—along with hamburger, green pepper, water chestnuts and pears. These were the foods studies had determined were the least likely to cause an allergic reaction. This was Phase One of an elimination diet to determine what foods, if any, Darren might be allergic to that could affect his behavior.

"I'd rather have Cheerios®," Andrea said, wrinkling her nose.

"So would Darren," I said grimly, wondering if Darren would ever again be allowed any input as to what he would like to eat.

The elimination diet sounded bad enough on paper, but in practice it turned out to be a nightmare. Here was this skinny little three year old who didn't care all that much about eating anyway, and once we started the diet, it seemed as though he was becoming skinnier and skinnier before our very eyes. Hamburger, green beans, green pepper, water chestnuts and pears were foods that he liked reasonably well, but understandably, not for *every* meal. I tried everything I could think of to entice him to eat: making a happy face on his hamburger with pieces of green pepper or building a green bean fence to corral water chestnut "sheep." I even resorted to bribes and threats. The first couple of evenings the rest of us had hamburger, green beans, green pepper, water chestnuts and pears also, but that didn't make any difference to Darren either. He would just pick at his food or refuse to eat it altogether.

Probably for the first time in his life he was actually *hungry*. He asked for candy. He wanted some catsup for his hamburger. He begged for some bread. Most of all, he wanted a drink of milk. Oh, just one sip of milk! The rest of us suffered right along with him since we had no choice. Darren was not one to suffer in silence. We were careful not to eat foods he liked around him, but that didn't help him forget about all the foods he could no longer have on this experimental diet.

He had an episode of vomiting the third day of the diet. I immediately called P.A.C. and learned that the vomiting was probably a withdrawal symptom. This was sometimes a reaction for people who had a problem with assimilation of sugar. The director encouraged me to continue with the diet.

Tom had been watching uneasily from the sidelines and decided it was time to call a halt. He felt that continuing the diet could be harmful to Darren, no matter what they said at P.A.C.

I didn't feel inclined to argue. Carrying the diet all the way through to the end with Darren — and probably any other three year old — was very close to impossible, to my way of thinking.

But in the interest of science I decided to go on the diet myself, just to see what might happen. Maybe I would learn something that would help Darren. Good old Mom!

According to the information about the elimination diet, withdrawal symptoms could range from mild to rather severe and might even be somewhat bizarre. One little boy reacted so violently that his parents actually had to restrain him for a few hours to prevent him from hurting himself. The most common reaction was extreme exhaustion and wanting to sleep. The severity of the symptoms usually peaked by the second or third day into the diet; therefore I scheduled my venture so those days would fall on the weekend — when Tom would be home to take over with the kids if need be.

By Saturday I was feeling very, *very* tired — instead of my usual "just tired." I dragged around all morning doing necessary chores while Tom puttered in his workshop in the garage.

"I've got to have a nap this afternoon. Will you be around to keep tabs on the kids?" I asked when he stepped into the kitchen for a cool drink late in the morning.

"Yeah, okay. I'll stay around," he said and went back to the garage.

After lunch I put Darren in bed for a nap and settled myself on the sofa with a thick volume from the P.A.C. library on childhood nutrition. Andrea was playing with her dolls in her room. I didn't expect to stay awake long enough to do much reading, but who cared? What a luxurious feeling to know that I didn't have to stay awake. Tom was on duty.

My eyelids were becoming very heavy when Tom came strolling through the family room with his briefcase.

"I'm going in to the office to work for a while," he announced casually as he passed through, not even looking in my direction.

Something snapped inside me. Suddenly the thick volume on childhood nutrition was flying across the room toward my offending husband. It just missed his head and landed with a thud against the side door.

I definitely had his attention now, though I was as surprised as he was at what I had just done.

"You have a problem with my leaving?" he asked dryly, bending over to pick up the missile I'd just launched at him.

"Yes, I have a problem with you leaving!" I burst out hysterically. "But I didn't mean to throw that book at you," I added with contrition.

He slapped his hand against his forehead. "Oh! Joyce! I"m sorry! I forgot you wanted to take a nap!"

I told him peevishly that it was not a case of "wanting to." I *had* to because I was *utterly* exhausted! With that, I laid back down on the sofa, my face to the wall, pulled the throw over my head and that was the last I remembered until I woke up in the quiet dark of the living room.

The clock said twelve-thirty and apparently everyone had gone to bed. I felt drained, but also somehow rested and at peace.

And so, with that instance of uncontrolled violence, passed my withdrawal.

Now began the process of adding different foods one at a time, waiting two days to see if there were any reactions to the new food, then adding yet another one.

I declared it rugged, but I suffered more or less in silence while appreciating that Tom and Andrea were sympathetic enough to at least be apologetic when they ate something I enjoyed but couldn't have.

I soon discovered that my suffering was not in vain as I continued with the diet. I was beginning to feel better than I had felt in years! Miraculously, the tiredness that had plagued me for so long was gone! And it stayed gone, as long as I was eating "just plain old food" as Andrea called it—meat, vegetables, fruit and whole grains. When I started adding in the "good stuff"—junk food—the old exhaustion would come back again.

If there was any one message that stood out strong in the nutritional materials from P.A.C., it was the magnitude of the problem that sugar and sugar substitutes like aspartame and sucralose can cause in the diets of many people. Certain studies seemed to indicate that all kinds of problems—from mild depression to downright criminal violence—could be attributed to a person's reaction to sugar.

Though I had not vomited those first days as Darren had, because of my violent outburst I was now convinced that sugar was a problem for me. I decided that the whole family would probably be better off without it too and wanted to at least give it a try.

It would have been a simple matter to merely announce that henceforth and forevermore this family would not be eating sugar. But with Andrea old enough to be out in the big wide world where sugary snacks are a way of life, I felt the campaign had to be one of education... and persuasion.

Tom was willing to go along with the program...at least at home. ("I can be sneaky at work if I get hungry for something sugary," he confided.) So we called a family council.

"We're going to try an experiment," I announced, knowing that the big word would capture Andrea's attention. More than likely this would all be beyond Darren's comprehension, but he wasn't really the problem at this point. I began to explain just what an experiment was and how—and why—we would conduct ours while both kids listened wide-eyed.

"Oh! Like those boys in the Bible storybook!" Andrea interrupted halfway through my discourse.

The boys in the Bible storybook? Tom and I looked questioningly at each other.

Andrea wriggled down from the stool where she had been perched and ran to get the Bible storybook I read to her and Darren at bedtime.

Returning with the book, she put it on the stool and leafed through its pages until she came to the story of Daniel.

"Right there, remember?" she asked, tapping the page with her finger. "Daniel and his friends didn't want to eat the king's junk food. They didn't want to do it just to get along with the king. They knew that their food was better so they did an experiment and just ate vegetables and good stuff while everyone else went along with the king and ate his food. And Daniel and his friends ended up looking healthier than everyone else!" Andrea ended triumphantly.

That clinched it. Why should we go along with the mainstream diet if it's not good for us just to get along? What was good enough for Daniel, Shadrach, Meshach and Abednego was good enough for the Jones family!

The four of us went through the kitchen cupboards, scouting out anything with sugar in it.

We loaded two grocery bags with cereals, mixes and snacks, including a bag of suckers and hard candies I had kept as special rewards for good behavior and treats, plus a canister of sugar. The kids and I watched while Tom locked the two bags in the trunk of the car he drove to work. When the two weeks that we had allotted for our experiment had passed, we would decide what to do with their contents. Maybe we would bring it back into the house — maybe we would get rid of it all.

The only bad stuff we found in the refrigerator was the catsup and mayonnaise, a jar of pickles and several bottles of salad dressing. These we put into a plastic bag fastened with a red tie which we put at the very back on the bottom shelf. The freezer was quite another matter with ice cream, baked goodies and who knew what else, so we decided to just leave that for the time being.

We all promised that for the next two weeks we would not eat anything with sugar in it. Not at home, not at school, not at work or anywhere else. I looked to see if Tom had his fingers crossed but he didn't.

"Not even a small piece of candy someone gives me?" Andrea amended with a meaningful look toward Darren.

Darren said, "Huh?" and wrinkled his nose at his sister.

"We"ll just have to watch him," I said, "and tell Cathy too."

I had a little trouble packing Andrea's lunch the next morning. It didn't seem like a proper school lunch without cookies but I had some nice apples. One of those would do nicely for dessert. I would go to the grocery store that very day to find suitable substitutes for cookies.

So after dropping Darren off at P.A.C., I drove to the supermarket where I usually shopped. Finding nothing in the way of suitable school lunch goodies, I decided to stop at Nature's Corner, a health food store on the way home.

Health food stores had always seemed like a kind of never-never land that I associated with straggly-haired, emaciated-looking hippie-type people carrying placards promoting some ecological issue—so I stepped into Nature's Corner with the feeling that I was entering a foreign country.

The woman behind the counter looked perfectly normal and in robust health. Several equally normal, healthy appearing customers came and went as I made my selections from an amazing array of food—some packaged and some in bins and huge jars—most of it completely free from sugar as well as all the chemicals and other harmful substances that I had so innocently been feeding my family all these years. And so the cupboards and the refrigerator at the Jones house took on a whole new look.

CHAPTER 15

The Pay Off

One afternoon after school — not quite two weeks into our no-sugar experiment — I took the kids along on an errand across town. It was a wonderful fall day and in spite of the usual city traffic, I felt somehow enveloped in an unaccustomed feeling of tranquility.

Tranquility! Tranquility had never before been a word I would have used to describe a drive with Darren and Andrea. It was usually an occasion for eventual mayhem in the back seat. For one awful moment the sensation swept over me that somehow I had left the kids behind, or that they had mysteriously disappeared from the back seat.

But,no, a quick glance assured me that they were there all right, sitting *quietly*, the picture of...yes, tranquility! I could scarcely believe my eyes and was puzzled at first as to what could have brought about this miracle. Then it hit me...could it be the change in diet?

"Oh surely not," Tom countered when I told him about our drive and the miraculous change in our children's behavior. But over the next few days, I observed that there actually *was* a change in the behavior of both children. Not that they had suddenly become model children, but the hyperactivity — the "wound up too tightly" behavior that we had thought was just something we had to live with—had lessened and sometimes was actually replaced by what could only be described as an unusual tranquility.

The clincher came when it dawned on me that Andrea wasn't arriving home from kindergarten in a state of near hysteria anymore. I had my little girl back again!

Now that I was convinced that the diet was working, there was no way that I was going to bring those two grocery bags of junk food back into the house. With a twinge of guilt, I dropped them off at the Salvation Army Food Pantry. Well not everyone wanted to cut out sugar, I consoled myself. They would get it somewhere and I did hate to throw away food that someone else could use.

Tom didn't see that eliminating sugar had made any difference in the way *he* felt, but he could also see that it *had* made a difference in the kids and he was really pleased to have a wife who didn't drag around half dead anymore. He was perfectly willing to more or less go along with the diet although he did eat what was left of the forbidden things in the refrigerator and freezer. And he just might be indulging away from home when he felt like it.

Things went along well as far as the diet was concerned for a while until I noticed that every now and then, Andrea's old after school hysteria would return. She had entered into the whole change in diet so enthusiastically that I couldn't believe she would cheat. But when I questioned her one afternoon when she had come home in an unusually belligerent mood, Andrea burst into tears.

"I *like* sugar stuff, even if it makes me feel bad!" she sobbed. "And sometimes kids give me cookies and candy at school...and I eat them!" Then she abruptly stopped crying and asked me seriously, "That's dumb, isn't it?"

"Well, yes, it is," I agreed, "but I *do* know how you feel. Every time I go past the Dairy Bar I think about how good some ice cream covered with gooey hot fudge would taste and I'm afraid if someone handed me a hot fudge sundae, I would have a very hard time not eating it."

We decided between the two of us that often there is a price to pay in order to have something good happen and that a person has choices to make in this regard, as to whether she can—or is willing to—pay the price.

A few days later I discovered the startling affect my choice of food was having on me personally.

Tom was rummaging in the freezer after the kids had gone to bed—looking for a snack—and came upon a package of brownies looking very luscious with walnuts and mint frosting.

"Oh, mint brownies! My very favorite!" I exclaimed longingly, looking over his shoulder as he opened the package and put two generous squares on a paper napkin.

Not letting myself think about the little talk I'd had with Andrea just the other day about choices and paying a price, I played with the temptation to have just *one* brownie...in the interest of science, maybe? I rationalized that maybe sugar didn't really bother me after all. That maybe it was just the improved diet that was helping me feel so much better. Well, there was one way to find out. And besides, they looked so good I just couldn't resist.

So I quickly ate my version of the "forbidden fruit" that had first tempted Adam so very long ago. I was so disappointed because it didn't even seem to taste as good as I had anticipated that I foolishly had another piece—just to make sure it really wasn't as delicious as I had remembered it being.

Well, the ceiling didn't immediately fall in and I didn't lapse into a coma—or commit any further deeds of violence like throwing books at my husband. In fact, we spent a rather pleasant evening playing Scrabble.

As we were heading upstairs to get ready for bed a few hours later, Tom was recounting a funny story about something that had happened at work—and I suddenly realized that without reason and quite inexplicably...I had tears streaming down my face!

Tom looked at me in surprise. "What'd I say?" he asked with concern.

"Nothing!" I said sheepishly, feeling very foolish.

"Then what's the matter? Why are you crying?"

"I don't know! I just feel like crying!" I sobbed helplessly as I sat down on the edge of our bed, completely powerless to stop the flow of tears or explain the acute feeling of depression welling up inside me. Nothing like this had ever happened to me before. Then suddenly — in the midst of my tears and sadness — it dawned on me what must have caused this! What else could it be but those mint brownies?

I turned off the light and slid under the covers. Knowing the cause for my emotional upset made me feel a little better, though this undeniable proof that I had better leave sugar alone was very upsetting. But, it really was a small price to pay for my newly discovered — and much needed — energy. I could certainly live with that sacrifice. And chalk one up for Darren! If it weren't for him, I probably never would have discovered my problem and would have spent the rest of my life being tired. On the other hand, of course, if it weren't for Darren, I wouldn't need so much energy! Oh, well...still in my pseudo-depressed state, I didn't have what it took to deal with the implications of *that* thought.

* * * * *

As time passed we became more and more convinced that changing our eating habits had been a wise move, and on occasion our findings would be verified by professionals in the field of health and nutrition. Through a radio interview I learned of the work of Dr. Joel Wallach — physician, author, scientist and biomedical researcher. His writings and his research on nutritional supplements would reinforce and expand on what we were learning and became an important contribution to the well being of our family.

While continuing to search for answers to help Darren, I went to as many lectures on nutrition as I could find. A lecture by Barbara Reed Stitt that I attended was particularly fascinating. This was way back in the late 70's and now the information in that lecture can be read in her book *Food and Behavior*. She had come to an understanding of the relationship between food and behavior through her work as a probation officer. In her book she talks of her experiences and points out that "The connection between food and behavior is so basic that it is being overlooked by parents, the school system, counselors and most of the medical professionals." She explained how the lack of nutrition — caused by eating foods that are over processed, sweetened, chemically treated, stripped of nutrients and overcooked — has affected people's mental health. I took all of this in and my search continued for even more information.

I continue to find a multitude of scientific studies,* empirical data and educated opinions on how food intake and supplementation will affect physical, mental and emotional health. Searching for viable information and sifting out incorrect theories is a great challenge…and the searching and sifting never ends.

---

*Doctors and research scientists have developed a supplement that will direct your own stem cells to other cells in your body that are in need of repair or regeneration. In 2003, The Massachusetts Institute of Technology called this approach of supplying the body with nutrients that allow the body to heal itself one of the "10 emerging technologies that will change the world."

The technology, *glycoscience*, has already been shown to be beneficial in the treatment of many medical disorders including ADD, certain neurological conditions, arthritis, fibromyalgia, CP, MS, and some forms of cancer. In the 40 years I have studied nutrition, glycoscience is by far the most exciting and encouraging development I've seen in supplementation effectiveness and wellness.

Joyce

CHAPTER 16

Another Determined Parent

An article in a week-old newspaper that I hadn't gotten around to reading caught my attention one morning as I was doing some straightening up around the house. It concerned a severely handicapped boy who was on a program of patterning similar to the one Darren had been on before he was a year old, except that it was much more extensive. This child was four years old and had existed more or less as a vegetable. Now, according to his mother, with all day volunteer help to put him through the grueling regimen of exercises, he was beginning to show signs of improvement.

Because we had felt that patterning had been beneficial to Darren and knowing that it was a controversial treatment, I was pleased to read what seemed to be a clear-cut endorsement of it...until I got to the last paragraph of the article. The focus then turned to an interview with a pediatrician in the city who questioned the value of the program and finally raised the possibility that it could even be harmful. In his "esteemed" opinion, no *caring* parent would subject a child to patterning.

Angrily, I slammed the newspaper down and stomped to the telephone to call the newspaper.

"Why," I demanded, after being shuttled around to three different editors, "did you have to end that article in such a negative light?"

It was in the interest of presenting both sides of the story, the cool voice at the other end of the line responded.

"Both sides of the story! The opinion of a parent against the opinion of a pediatrician—you call that presenting both sides fairly?" We as parents had seen Darren develop normal crawling skills that had amazed his doctors. How could a pediatrician, who had not one ounce of proof that patterning could actually do harm, make such a statement? I didn't bother to wait for a response, but hung up and thumbed through the phone book to find the number of the family in the article.

And that was how I made the acquaintance of Joan Rhea, never realizing at the time the influence that phone conversation would have on our lives. It would be some time before we met face to face, but we chatted a number of times after that by telephone and became good friends.

Joan, a divorcee, was more or less on her own searching for that elusive something that might help her handicapped little boy. We have since come to realize that parents of handicapped children fall mainly into two categories—well, extremes would probably be more accurate. On the one hand, there are those who, though devastated by their child's problems, nevertheless seem to accept the tragedy—if not the child—with a fatalistic attitude: This is the way it is and there is nothing that can be done about it. Then there are those of us who are convinced that *somewhere*, if we look and try hard and long enough, there *is* something that will bring about a real change, if not a complete cure for our children.

Joan was right in the front ranks of this latter category. And we weren't far behind. She, too, was upset with the way the newspaper had handled the article. Her experience with the medical profession had been much the same as ours...discouraging. She had a vast store of horror stories of her own experiences as well as those of other parents she'd met in their quest for help for a handicapped child.

Nutrition was a very big thing with Joan, and she and I compared notes on our findings and exchanged the titles of books on the subject that we had each found helpful. We talked for nearly an hour that first conversation and when we finally said good-bye, we promised to keep in touch.

Through Joan I learned of a Dr. Lee who had a method of testing for food allergies without going through the impossible elimination diet that P.A.C. suggested. Dr. Lee, strangely enough, was an eye, ear, nose and throat M.D. whose office was in an osteopathic clinic — which was at that time an unusual combination.

One cold January day, Darren and I spent a bizarre afternoon in Dr. Lee's office. The testing consisted of putting concentrated drops of a certain food under Darren's tongue at ten-minute intervals. We settled down on a comfortable sofa and Darren listened quietly as I read to him while the drops were given time to be absorbed. With the first three foods, nothing happened. Suddenly, after the fourth set of drops, Darren jumped up from the sofa, grabbed one of the large cushions off the sofa and threw it across the room! Then he ran wildly around the room, jumping over the coffee table and crawling under chairs. Had there been a chandelier in the room, I was convinced he would have been swinging from it. I was glad only the nurse was in the room with us.

This went on for ten minutes until the nurse put more drops under Darren's tongue to neutralize whatever it was that had caused the reaction. Again, Darren sat down to listen quietly to the story.

I never would have believed his reaction had I not seen it with my own eyes even though by this time — after my experience with the P.A.C. elimination diet — I was convinced that food affected behavior. Now I had scientific support that Darren's sometimes erratic behavior was not necessarily due to lack of discipline as some people believed. If only I had a movie camera to document what I had seen!

It took three more sessions (and a good-sized chunk of Tom's paycheck) to complete the tests, which revealed that Darren was allergic to yellow food coloring, corn, chicken, eggs, milk and all refined foods, which included sugar of course. I had already eliminated the refined foods—junk food, strictly speaking, which no health conscious person should consume anyway because it has little, if any, nutritional value and can be harmful—and now added the others to the list of things for Darren to avoid.

However, Dr. Lee gave him some drops, which would act as a sort of vaccine to build up resistance to these foods in the hope that eventually he would be able to tolerate them in moderation. (After taking the drops for a couple of years, Darren was again tested and, other than the refined foods, he only showed a reaction to corn.)

CHAPTER 17

Searching Outside the Box

Joan Rhea called me one day fairly bursting with news. She had just returned from Minneapolis where she had attended a class on healing by the laying on of hands.

I remembered reading something about laying on of hands some time ago, but just what was involved I didn't know, except that it had some sort of religious connotation and at the time I would have described it as "weird."

Joan didn't have any miracles to report as yet, but by the time she had spent a half hour telling me about her experience in Minneapolis I was definitely interested in learning more about this healing method, though "weird" still hung in the back of my mind when I thought about it. To my surprise, Tom was intrigued with the idea.

The next week another class would convene. My brother and his wife, Bob and Cay, who lived in St. Paul, had been asking us to come up for a visit. We could visit and sightsee during the day, put the kids to bed with Bob and Cay there to keep an eye on them and go to the classes, which were held in the evening.

With a couple of long distance phone calls, it was all set. Bob and Cay seemed delighted to have us come and even insisted that we bring Muffin along. Now that was true hospitality!

Everything was working out so beautifully that we had the feeling that our going was providentially engineered. We packed for the trip with a feeling of great expectation and anticipation. Maybe this would be the breakthrough for Darren that we had been hoping and praying for! A miracle, even, perhaps?

We arrived late Monday afternoon. Cay, just starting dinner, was cutting up broccoli.

"Oh, Aunt Cay, may Muffin have that?" Andrea asked, pointing to the tough stalk that Cay was about to put in the garbage.

"Well, sure!" Cay answered, "but I didn't know dogs ate broccoli."

"Muffin does!" Andrea said proudly. "She thinks it's a green bone."

Actually, Muffin had only recently been introduced to broccoli—when a stalk fell on the floor at home. It had evidently looked like a bone to her and she had had a good time gnawing on it, finally eating it. So now, every time we had broccoli, Muffin got the tough stalks that otherwise would have gone in the garbage.

Muffin, being her usual adorable little self, sat up and begged when Andrea showed her the stalk.

"Broccoli's awfully good for people and dogs, too," Andrea commented as Muffin went off to a corner of the kitchen to enjoy her prize.

And speaking of what's good for people and dogs brought to Andrea's mind something else that she thought Aunt Cay would like to know.

"We aren't eating sugar and all that junky stuff at our house anymore," she announced.

Well, that was enough to get an incredulous look from Cay and spark a conversation that lasted most of the way through dinner. It hadn't occurred to me to mention our new diet and we felt really bad about that, knowing that Cay loved to cook and just now realizing that, not having been informed ahead of time, she would have baked up a whole stock of goodies to have on hand for us that would be loaded with "sugar and all that junky stuff."

* * * * *

The sun was almost setting as we drove slowly along a street of the Minneapolis suburb looking for the number of the house where the classes would be held. The neighborhood was quite ordinary with plain little one story houses differing from one another mainly in color. The address we were looking for turned out to be a nondescript white house with nothing to indicate that this was anything other than someone's residence except that there were several cars parked in front and in the driveway. When we rang the bell, the door was promptly opened and we were greeted by a woman who introduced herself as Evelyn, the instructor of the class.

The room into which we were ushered was furnished with metal folding chairs arranged in two semicircles, one behind the other, facing a tall stool. Most of the chairs were already occupied. We made our way to two empty chairs at the far end of the front row. Several more people arrived after we did, making twenty people in all.

When everyone had found a place, Evelyn gracefully seated herself on the stool in front of us. She sat without saying anything for several minutes, gazing thoughtfully above our heads, her hands folded in her lap. She was a quietly attractive but ordinary appearing woman. As to age, we would have guessed early fifties.

Turning her attention to her audience, her eyes rested briefly on each of us in a sort of silent salutation. Then, very softly, she began to speak.

For over three hours, with only a brief break at the halfway point, we sat absolutely mesmerized by this woman as she gave us the background of this particular discipline of healing by the laying on of hands— Its beginnings in the early 1900's with a university professor in Japan who discovered quite by accident that he possessed a wonderful power in his hands; the miraculous healings that came about as he learned to use this power; and his teaching the techniques to others.

This was what surprised us. We had thought healing was a spiritual gift, but here was a method that could be *learned*. Evelyn herself had traveled to Japan as a college student and studied under this man, who must have been a remarkably brilliant and compassionate person. We gathered that not just anyone would be a candidate to become a healer, though just what the requirements might be, she didn't come right out and say. There seemed to be a kind of intuitive selection.

The term, "Universal Energy" came up often during the evening's lecture. The way Evelyn described it, this Energy was an invisible, yet strangely tangible, power that could be channeled for the purpose of healing all manner of ills. She told of person after person who had been healed of both physical and mental illnesses.

It was after ten when Evelyn finished speaking. We all filed quietly out into the chilly night air as though still under a spell she'd woven.

This was heavy stuff that we'd been listening to this evening and it had left us with more questions than answers. Like this power—energy—that Evelyn kept talking about. Was that just another name for God? But she had said this method of healing wasn't a religion. Still, the power has to come from somewhere. And where else could it come from but God? It had a "religious" feel, somehow. Evelyn seemed like a good person, compassionate, loving, self-sacrificing, very caring about people, devoting her life to helping others.

Just think of having it within your power to *heal* people—to relieve suffering! Wouldn't you go to the nearest hospital and run up and down the halls healing everyone?

But Evelyn wasn't doing that. No one we knew of was. Even Jesus didn't go around healing everyone, did

He? Maybe healing isn't for everyone...if it was, no one would be sick or handicapped, would they?

But what if *we* could learn this laying on of hands? We didn't know if we could handle that, when it came right down to it, wonderful as it could be. We thought we'd almost rather believe that it all was fakery. Then we wouldn't have to deal with it.

Still, if it was the real thing and Darren could be healed...Oh! Then we would learn to deal with it!

Cay and Bob were waiting up for us, eager to hear about our evening, so over hot tea we answered their questions, which were all asking more or less the same thing—Is it for real? We tried not to make what we had heard that evening sound too far out. Our nutritional revolution was enough to spring on them in one day.

We went to bed that night still trying to put the pieces of the evening together, but not getting very far. We would just have to wait and see.

CHAPTER 18

Thinking Outside the Box

For the second class session, Evelyn had promised a demonstration of actual healing. After some introductory remarks, she asked for a volunteer from the class. A middle aged man introduced himself simply as John. He came up and sat on a low stool in front of her.

"My first task," she said, "is to determine the source of John's illness. He is suffering from what several doctors had diagnosed as a duodenal ulcer. However, as I explained last evening, our illnesses do not necessarily originate from the spot where we feel the pain."

With that brief explanation, Evelyn turned her full attention to her patient, quietly questioning him as she laid her hands systematically in different positions on his head, neck and back.

"Yes, I am getting a blockage here," she would say, "I feel coldness." Or, "I feel energy flowing from my hands. Healing is taking place in this area."

All the while, besides the questioning of the man seated in front of her, she seemed to be carrying on a conversation with someone else. This was spoken so softly that we couldn't catch much of what she said. It seemed that she would ask a question, pause for an answer and sometimes make a verbal response or confirmation, or simply change the position of her hands as though someone were directing her movements.

Gradually we became aware of a faint fragrance, sweet and spicy, like carnations. Was it someone's perfume? But why hadn't we noticed it before? No one new had come into the room. Then suddenly, I noticed strange shadows on the wall behind Evelyn. I turned quickly to see what could be making them, thinking it must be someone behind us since it was not Evelyn or the man in the chair.

Evelyn glanced at me. "What are you seeing?" she asked.

"It…looks like…like shadows of some men on the wall," I stammered, embarrassed to have distracted Evelyn and to have attention focused on me.

"Yes," Evelyn responded matter-of-factly, "those are my guides—my spirit helpers. Probably most of you won't see them." Again, she turned her attention back to her patient.

A questioning rustle swept across the two rows of people watching. When we glanced at each other, I knew instantly that Tom was not seeing Evelyn's guides and maybe was wondering about my sanity, or at least my eyesight, at this point. However, there were several people nodding their heads, indicating that they too were seeing the shadows.

We watched—at first uneasily and skeptically—then spellbound, as Evelyn worked with two more people that evening. The next one was Alice, a woman of perhaps fifty who had arthritis.

At Evelyn's prompting, she showed us that her hands were becoming deformed. Her stiff and hesitant movements and the lines on her face were silent, but obvious, indicators of the pain that was also a part of her suffering.

With John, the man with the ulcer, one could imagine that perhaps he looked more relaxed, but we had to take his word for it when he said he felt better when Evelyn had finished with him as there was no visible or tangible proof. But when she worked on Alice, before our very eyes the deformity of her hands disappeared and we could believe her when she happily exclaimed that the pain was gone.

An aura of excitement enveloped us.

The last subject was Monica, a woman of perhaps twenty—thin, unattractive, unkempt—whom we had noticed the night before. She seemed shut up inside herself and extremely uncomfortable and ill at ease as she now became the center of attention of the class. Her voice was harsh and she had such a severe impediment in her speech that it was difficult to understand what she said in response to Evelyn's questioning.

Evelyn looked up momentarily from her patient toward the door that had been left open because of the mildness of the evening and with surprising urgency she asked Tom to close it. He did so promptly.

Evelyn continued with her examination, at first seeming to find only blockages and doing a great deal of consulting with her "guides." I became aware of an increase in the shadow activity on the wall behind her. All the while, Monica was becoming more and more agitated, occasionally groaning. Then suddenly she cried out and we all froze in terror because it was not Monica's voice... but a strange and frightening *masculine* voice that was loud and threatening!

We were too startled to wonder if we were in danger or even make sense of what was going on as Evelyn engaged the voice in a verbal battle that eventually ended quite abruptly.

Then, with her hands at Monica's temples, Evelyn closed her eyes as if she was in deep concentration. A tense silence hovered over us permeated by that strange spicy-sweet carnation fragrance that was so strong now we could almost taste it. Then with a look of triumph Evelyn whispered that energy was beginning to flow.

Monica gradually quieted, her agitation visibly draining away. Then with a little cry and a violent shudder that shook off Evelyn's hands, she fell forward limply.

Tom and another man jumped up to catch her before she hit the floor.

Supported by the men, one on each side of her, she stood looking dazed for a moment, then stepped back, smiled a beautiful smile and said clearly in a soft, almost musical voice, "Thank you! I'm all right now!"

"Yes, you are!" Evelyn exclaimed, rushing to her and giving her a big hug while tears streamed down her face.

We could see through our own tears that she really was all right! Something wonderful had happened to that thin, unattractive girl who had sat before us only minutes ago. The straggly hair and drab clothing didn't matter. Something significant *had* changed...it was like some repressive force had been lifted. The harshness of her voice and the impediment were gone as proof of it all, but that was only a small token of what had taken place here.

Someone began to clap and we all joined in with tears streaming down our faces. It was the only way we could think of to express the emotions we were feeling.

"Let's find out if Evelyn will see Darren," Tom said, leaning close to me so I could hear over the clapping.

I nodded. We still had unanswered questions, but after what we had just witnessed none of them seemed relevant. Here—perhaps at last!—was help for our little boy. Yes, what we had just witnessed was a bit frightening to say the least. Evelyn's "guides" were definitely "weird." But still...there *was* a spirit world. Even the Bible taught that, didn't it? And these spirits were doing good! So, what could be the harm?

We had to wait for nearly a half hour to talk with Evelyn. Evidently others in the class wanted to talk about private healings too.

"Yes, I would like to see your little son," Evelyn said when we described Darren's disabilities. "I may be able to help, though I dare not make any promises. We shall have to wait and see."

She puzzled over her notebook for a moment. The last class was Thursday night and her schedule was already filled until then. She finally gave us an appointment for Friday at eight o'clock in the morning. That was the only time she could work us in. She had a plane to catch at eleven. Gratefully, we thanked her and said goodnight.

On the drive back to Cay and Bob's we talked about Evelyn's wanting the outside door closed. She must have been expecting what happened. It certainly would have been cause for alarm if the neighbors had heard that awful dialogue—as it was for us! Plus, had it been open, we decided we might have been tempted to escape into the safety of the real world. We were glad Cay and Bob didn't stay up for a report on our evening. How could we possibly have described what we had witnessed?

As we took our seats for class the next evening we couldn't help but notice Monica, the young woman who had been healed the night before. She was quite a different person from the one we had seen at the first two classes. Besides being neat and attractive, there was a sort of glow about her as she sat across the room carrying on an animated conversation with the couple seated in front of her.

Either she was an excellent actress or we had witnessed a real miracle. We leaned toward the miracle. We wanted so much for this laying on of hands to be the answer to *our* prayers—that wonderful thing that would make all the difference for Darren. We *NEEDED* a miracle. How could Darren be all right without one?

Class that evening consisted of a lecture on the techniques of making miracles happen—exactly how to go about laying hold of the Energy that Evelyn was always talking about. It seemed almost sacrilegious to connect such a lofty thing with methods and techniques. Yet it was exciting to think that here at the disposal of humankind was a tool that could be used to help others if only we could accept it and learn to use it. What a really beautiful thing it would be if because of Darren we, or even one of us, could learn to heal! And this would be the beginning of many healings…other children handicapped like Darren and perhaps even Joan's little boy.

Evelyn had made it clear all along that not everyone who learned the techniques actually became a healer. Still, according to Evelyn, the Energy was everywhere just waiting to be tapped. If one could somehow harness the Energy people would recognize it. No need to advertise… they would be sought after.

CHAPTER 19

Wondering About the Box

Evelyn had told us with a twinkle in her eye that the last class would be a "hands on" experience. The whole thing was pretty awe inspiring, like treading on holy ground, so we drove across Minneapolis to the meeting that evening with trepidation. We weren't sure we belonged on holy ground.

The session began with Evelyn reminding us that being able to heal by the laying on of hands was not for everyone, that there was no fixed criteria of what it took to make a healer. It was more than merely learning the techniques, but just what else was involved she never did make clear. The only way to discover whether one actually had this gift, she told us, was to try. People who thought they could not possibly have the gift might be surprised to discover that they did after all.

Evelyn paired us off—but not as husband and wife teams—and situated us around the room.

The first step was getting in touch with the Energy, which after all we had heard of it, we felt should be spelled with that capital E. Was it really another name for God? If it was, then we really *were* on holy ground!

It seemed logical to us that being able to get in touch with the Energy was what separated the healers from the observers.

Evelyn spoke quietly, instructing us step by step to prepare ourselves to be recipients of the Energy. What she was saying was not new by this time. She had spoken a great deal in the lecture the first night about this preparation and receiving and she had demonstrated it. But this was the real thing—even though our patients were only fellow students.

As I stood concentrating and following Evelyn's instruction, I became aware of the spicy-sweet fragrance, though it was only very faint. I wondered if Evelyn's "guides" were there too although I didn't dare turn around to look. And if so, would they also be my guides now? I wasn't sure that I wanted them.

We spent over a half hour following the prescribed procedure under the supervision of Evelyn...all with no flow of anything except conversation.

When it was all over, we felt drained and disappointed. We never did find out if anything exciting happened to anyone else. The session just sort of melted to an end, and we found ourselves driving numbly back across town.

There was still Darren's appointment tomorrow. Had we been foolish to make it?

As we always did with both Andrea and Darren, we had tried to prepare Darren for the consultation, though we had no idea how to explain exactly what might take place since we didn't know ourselves.

Evelyn met us at the door, led us through the living room and into a little back room. Bright sunlight streamed through its one window. The only furnishings in the room were a couple of straight chairs and an examining table which was enough to convince Darren that this was a doctor's office. He began to whimper and cling to Tom. "No! No! No!" he cried, working up to a fine crescendo.

"No, nothing!" Tom said, picking him up and setting him on the table.

"It's all right, remember?" I said. "The nice lady will talk to you."

Darren was still clinging to Tom as he looked warily at the "nice lady" who was taking something out of a small black velvet drawstring bag.

"I need you to hold this for me, Darren," she said, showing him the large piece of yellowish crystal she had taken from her bag. It was perhaps six inches high and cut in such a way that the light shining through it made little rainbows inside. We wondered if he would be able to see it well enough to notice the rainbows, but whatever he was able to see evidently fascinated him and he reached for it eagerly.

"This was given to me long ago by a Japanese man whom I had healed," Evelyn said, talking now to us. "'What shall I do with this beautiful thing?' I wondered. Then one day a message of knowledge came to me: 'Use it in your work.' And so I do...when it is needed," she finished with a smile in Darren's direction.

Darren was now sitting on the table with his legs dangling, fondling the crystal, bringing it close to his face, moving it away again, turning it first one way and then another. Evelyn motioned us to the chairs and then stepped to the other side of the table behind Darren. She quietly contemplated the wall in front of her for a minute or so, her hands relaxed on the table. Then she placed her hands on Darren's head. He shook his head as though to shake them off.

"Darren, Darren," Evelyn said in a soft singsong voice, not moving her hands. She proceeded with her routine, occasionally talking softly more to herself than to Darren or us. We noticed no carnation fragrance this time and I didn't see Evelyn's guides if they were on hand.

Evelyn spent a great deal of time working on Darren's head, removing her hands from one position and then returning them again to the same spot. Once when she had spent some time on the area just behind his ears, he shivered, looked at us and wrinkled his nose. Then he turned his attention back to the crystal, which amazingly kept him occupied during the rest of the session.

"He is so young," Evelyn said when she had finished, "we shall have to wait and see what has taken place here today. Miracles do not always come instantly. Sometimes they come a little at a time."

A little at a time. We were willing to accept that. We would have preferred an instant miracle, but a little at a time would be better than nothing at all!

CHAPTER 20

The Big Wheel

Spring came and life went on just as though we had never been to Minneapolis. The "waiting and seeing" turned out to be just waiting and seeing nothing much in the way of improvement for Darren except what could just as easily be attributed to something else — the change in diet, the training at P.A.C. — or maybe it was only maturity. Darren *would* soon be four years old!

The question of what to get Darren for his birthday was settled when he went with Tom to a hardware store that also sold toys. Darren spotted a sporty Big Wheel trike and he immediately climbed on. Although he didn't know how to pedal it, he had a wonderful time with the handlebars.

At home was a tricycle that Andrea had outgrown but Darren had never been interested in that. He couldn't seem to figure out how to work the pedals, and we thought perhaps with his sight problem he felt insecure perched on that little seat with nothing around him but those thin handle bars. But he was definitely very interested in this low-to-the-ground vehicle and it was only with a great ruckus that Tom was able to pull him off of it so they could go home.

By the time they arrived home, Darren still hadn't forgiven Tom for separating him from the new love of his life.

"Bike!" he kept saying over and over, sometimes in a pitifully sad little voice with tears not far behind and other times in a not so little voice that threatened violence if the coveted object did not appear immediately.

So Tom bought the Big Wheel the day before Darren's birthday and came thumping into the house with it just before dinnertime.

The moment Darren caught sight of that bike, all thoughts of dinner and eating evaporated. "Bike!" he screamed and climbed on, determined to nevermore be parted. While the rest of us ate, Darren went on a long, tortuous drive which required a lot of wrestling with the handlebars but didn't get him much of anywhere. I did manage to spoon a few mouthfuls of food into him before he discovered that he could make the bike move by walking his feet on the floor. Tom tried to show him what the pedals were for but Darren wasn't interested — feet on the floor worked just fine.

Poor Muffin, after several close calls with the reckless driver on the Big Wheel, hid in her safety zone behind the sofa and stayed there until Darren had at last had enough traveling for the day and climbed off to see what Tom was doing in his workshop.

On Sunday morning — the day of his birthday — Darren finally figured out what the pedals on his bike were for, so we had a great deal of trouble separating him from the Big Wheel when it was time to go to church. When we got home, he jumped back on it again immediately as though drawn by a magnet.

As the day progressed, Darren's prowess improved and by evening he was pedaling forward and backward with ease. Anything in the way became an endangered species, so poor Muffin took up permanent residence behind the sofa.

He did stop riding it long enough to eat a little dinner that night and I was pleased that he also took time out to admire his birthday cake. I had baked it especially for him and it was shaped like a little train. The base was Boston Brown bread (no sugar!) baked in three cans so there was an engine, a coal car and a caboose. Smoke made of popcorn threaded on an appropriately shaped paper clip puffed from the engine; the coal car was filled with "coal" raisins and four red candles rode on the caboose.

On Tuesday Darren's mean mother (that being me) issued an ultimatum: The Big Wheel was no longer considered an indoor toy. I took him and his vehicle outside and showed him that he could ride it on the concrete driveway and on the sidewalk in front of the house as long as he didn't go any farther than our driveway on one side and the fence where Martin's yard began on the other. He had learned to stay pretty much where he was supposed to be when on foot and now he did equally well with the Big Wheel.

CHAPTER 21

Sailing and Fishing with Howdy Doody

Summer that year was pleasant and relaxed thanks to Cathy Peterson, whose great joy in life seemed to be keeping Darren and all the other younger children in the neighborhood entertained. I wondered how I had ever managed without her. Sometimes five or six youngsters came to play, but no problem! Cathy was in charge.

For three weeks early in the summer, Andrea and Darren took swimming lessons. This was Andrea's third year of instruction and she was becoming an excellent swimmer. Darren was a beginner and at first a very reluctant learner.

In a magazine article about teaching children to swim I had read that the temperature of the water, not surprisingly, affected how quickly and how well young children learned to swim. Certainly this would be an especially important consideration for our skinny little Darren who had no insulating body fat. Therefore we were pleased to find private lessons for him in a heated pool. Still it was with some misgivings that I handed him over to the instructor, a personable male college student.

Darren stood shivering at the edge of the pool clutching his towel around him as if it were his only hope of survival. I watched from a distance as the young man jollied him into the pool—minus the towel. The next thing I knew Darren was happily mimicking the instructor and "learning to be a fish."

When the lesson was over, he was no longer a reluctant swimmer. Now his towel was only for drying and not security. That summer in the comfortably warm pool, he learned to love the water. Because of the deep breathing techniques he had learned at P.A.C.—breathing into that plastic bag for carefully determined periods of time to increase brain function and lung capacity if you've forgotten—he was able to swim underwater the width of the pool and even retrieve colorful painted rocks at the bottom. Quite a feat for a four year old...and especially so for *our* four year old!

In July, the kids and I spent two weeks at Blue Lake about fifty miles north of Stanton. Tom's sister and her husband had offered us the use of their cabin at no cost. How could we refuse an offer like that? Tom was working but came up on weekends.

The cabin was charmingly rustic with only the basic modern conveniences—electricity, cold running water and a flush toilet. If anyone wanted a warm bath, water had to be heated on an ancient electric stove. But who cared? We could take our baths in the lake and a wonderful screened-in porch facing the lake more than made up for any lack of conveniences.

At least twice a day, the kids and I went to the swimming area a half a block away to enjoy the beach. Andrea could have happily spent all her time in the lake practicing the strokes she had learned in her swimming lessons or just splashing in the water. But Darren, although he had learned to enjoy playing in the *pool*, had some reservations about all that water in the lake. Plus it wasn't warm like the pool. After several attempts though, I did get him into the water by standing behind him and backing him in so he could *see* that dry land was safely near by and feel secure. What he liked best was digging in the sand—but not the wet sand by the water that stuck to him. "Ucky!" he would mutter with distaste, brushing the sand from his hands and bare legs.

I thought going fishing would be fun for both Andrea and Darren and decided that the sand bar on the other side of the lake recommended by the man at the bait shop would be a good place for beginners.

So late one afternoon—armed with bamboo poles, a supply of minnows from the bait shop and a little plastic pail to carry home our catch (just in case!)—we set off. Once we got there I sat down at the end of the dock and put Andrea on one side of me and Darren on the other. They dangled their bare feet in the water while I opened the carton of minnows and proceeded to bait the hooks.

"Little tiny fish!" Andrea exclaimed. Darren was equally fascinated with the minnows so he was reluctant to part with the one I had put on his hook, but finally he followed Andrea's example and tossed it into the water.

"Now we have to wait and see what happens," I told them, hoping that there was at least one alert and hungry fish down there that would take the bait before Darren's patience ran out.

And there was! After just a short wait Darren's line jerked.

"Darren! Pull up your line!" I urged while I helped him pull in his catch. It was a rather small fish but definitely not the minnow I had put on the hook.

Darren looked at his fish in amazement. "It grew!" he exclaimed, evidently thinking that some wonderful magic had been performed on the minnow under the water to turn it into a bigger fish and no amount of explaining could persuade him otherwise.

We had brought our sailboat with us to the lake. It was a very small craft and perfectly flat—basically a surfboard with a sail. Tom had bought it before we were married and in our early years before the kids were born we had become fair-to-good sailors and sailing had been one of our favorite pastimes. Knowing the boat was there, the kids soon started begging to go fishing on the sailboat and after a bit of consideration I decided, "Why not?'

First the boat had to be dragged about thirty feet to the water—not an easy task with only one adult and two children—but we were motivated and got it there. While I did the rigging, I was beginning to wonder if perhaps fishing from the sailboat was more than I could manage. Could I handle two small children, the rudder, the line to the sail and the bamboo poles? I baited the hooks and this time the bait was worms so there wouldn't be any confusion about the bait growing into a full size fish. That done, Andrea settled herself on the front of the boat with her pole. At least she could handle her own pole. Then Darren and I got on behind Andrea with Darren sitting between us and as close as possible to me. I held on to the back strap of his life jacket with one finger, the sail line running through the same hand. My other hand was on the rudder. It was soon obvious that the bamboo pole was going to be too much for Darren to manage in this situation so the only possibility was between my toes. I decided that would work and off we went, a beautiful breeze gently carrying us back and forth and not too far out onto the lake. At first Darren was finding our fishing expedition rather dull, except for having to dodge the sail whenever I turned the boat about, but then his pole started to jerk.

"Darren, raise your pole!" Andrea and I both shouted, "you've got a fish!"

With a little help from me—who really didn't have a hand to spare—he pulled up a small sunfish just barely hanging on the hook. As soon as it was out of the water, it jumped off the hook and landed on the boat deck where it flipped and flopped and flipped and flopped. Andrea and Darren frantically attempted to prevent its escape while I had all I could do to keep the boat upright.

"Catch it! Catch it!" we were all shouting. But after an exciting few minutes the fish, with one grand flip, flopped back into the water, earning itself the title of "The Fish That Got Away." Now Darren had that story, along with the one about The Fish That Grew, to tell Dad when he came up the next weekend.

The kids and I drove into town Friday afternoon to do some grocery shopping at the supermarket for the weekend.

Darren, riding in the shopping cart, caught the attention of a friendly stock boy and they entertained each other while Andrea and I rummaged through a bin of bargains.

"Your little boy reminds me of somebody and I can't think who," the young man said as we started to move on.

Then in the produce department the same stock boy came hurrying down the aisle, obviously looking for us.

"Now I know who it is," he announced with a triumphant grin, "It's Howdy Doody!" He patted Darren on the shoulder. "You put strings on him and you"ll get rich!"

"Who's Howdy Doody?" Andrea wanted to know as the young man disappeared through a swinging door at the back of the store.

I explained that he was a ventriloquist's dummy that used to be on television, probably when the young man was her age.

"Well Darren doesn't need strings," Andrea said.

When Tom arrived at the lake late that afternoon, Andrea recounted the Howdy Doody story.

"Strings, huh, Darren?" he mused. "We"ll have to remember that!"

Darren shook his head. He had no idea what all this talk about strings meant.

Early that evening, we all went down to the beach for a swim. The day had been warm and Tom, Andrea and I all thought the water was wonderfully refreshing.

But Darren thought it was too cold and spent most of the time shivering and playing in the sand. Finally, concerned about his shivering, I went up on shore, swathed him in a fluffy beach towel and sat down on a bench with him on my lap.

"Now there's nothing left but your nose and your toes," I said, "and I see big toes and little toes."

"Yeah," he said, bending his knee to bring that foot closer so he could see it better. Wriggling a hand out from under the towel he pointed to his little toe. "That one," he said solemnly, "didn't grow. Didn't eat enough."

CHAPTER 22

A Rainbow Too Late

Fall came and we settled back into our school routine with Andrea in first grade now and Darren still at P.A.C.

One day while talking to the manager of the heath food store, I learned about another rainbow to pursue — cranial adjustments. According to this manager, they were done routinely in Europe on newborns in the event of birth injuries. Then he mentioned that an elderly female osteopath in town, Dr. Anna Slocum, performed them and told me about a number of children's problems that she had helped. One was a baby girl, born with a grossly misshapen head, who had been brought to her as a last resort. Specialists had told her parents surgery was the only thing to try but it was risky and might not even do any good. After being treated by Dr. Slocum, the baby no longer needed to be subjected to surgery since she was developing normally.

A week later, Darren and I were in Dr. Slocum's office.

The doctor had just begun to examine Darren when she said in a quiet, compassionate voice, "Oh, my! If only I had seen him *earlier!*"

Something inside me slowly died as the doctor went on to explain that cranial adjustments for problems such as Darren's can be quite effective...but they had to be done in infancy before the closing of the fontanel.

If only we had known!

Then I remembered pleading with the University Hospital doctors when Darren was three months old — asking them about some suggestion — any suggestion — as to treatments we might try. Surely they had known about Dr. Slocum's work! WHY hadn't they said anything? "Then it's too late for you to do anything?" I asked her in anguish.

"Well, perhaps not quite," Dr. Slocum said. She explained that the bones in a child's skull are not yet fused and can be manipulated to some degree. "I think I can help a little, mainly in stimulating the pituitary gland."

I remembered from my college studies the importance of the pituitary gland, called the master of the glands because it serves to regulate all the others. This was an area the specialists had focused on in their studies of Darren's problems, though they had not offered even one suggestion as to what might be done with it that might help.

Dr. Slocum began Darren's treatment that very day.

Driving home, the doctor's words haunted me, "If only I had seen him earlier!" I glanced at Darren sitting by me in his seat. Was his whole life going to be a constant search for help that was either found too late or not at all? Had we known about Dr. Slocum when he was a baby would things have been different?

"Oh, Darren, I"m sorry! So very sorry!" I agonized silently over and over again.

When the kids were in bed that night, I poured out my grief and bitterness to Tom as I told him about the visit with Dr. Slocum.

Four years too late! Surely, the doctors at University Hospital knew about cranial adjustments. Why didn't they tell us and let us make the decision whether to try it or not? *Why?*

We had to believe that there was a purpose for what we'd been through, but what purpose could there have been in the doctors having withheld information that might have helped? We learned since that Dr. Slocum *was* well known for her work with children and was a pioneer in her field. And recently we also learned of another treatment for microcephalics that was being used successfully at the time Darren was born—surgical placement of plates in the skull to prevent premature closing of the fontanel, which is what had occurred with Darren. Why weren't we told about this procedure? About Dr. Slocum?

We brooded silently, finding no answer. Sadly, Dr. Slocum died before the course of Darren's treatment was finished, but we were referred to another fine doctor at the College of Osteopathic Medicine who treated Darren for about a year before he too passed away. After that we heard of Dr. DeJarnett in another state who was so well spoken of for his work with cranial adjustments with children, we felt it would be worthwhile to make the ten hour round trip for a consultation with him.

"I agree with Dr. Slocum. This is one of the most misshapen and misaligned heads I've ever seen," he announced after examining Darren. "But someone has done a lot of work with this boy because he is functioning at a much higher level than might be expected. However, there's nothing more that I can do for him...if only I had seen him much earlier, then maybe..."

At least we'd been doing something right! But unfortunately, nothing could ever change all those "if onlys."

CHAPTER 23

Brown Bread and Peer Pressure

Andrea seemed to be having a problem at school. Nearly every day she came home out of sorts. Not quite to the point that she had been in kindergarten when we had discovered her problem with sugar, but still, it seemed that all was not well.

One day I discovered an uneaten sandwich in her lunchbox. "Andrea, why didn't you eat your sandwich today?" I asked.

Andrea shrugged and mumbled something about not being hungry—which didn't sound like Andrea. After some probing, the truth came out. Andrea had not been eating her sandwiches for weeks. She had been throwing them away because the other kids teased her about the brown bread. But she had forgotten to throw away today's sandwich so now she had been discovered.

"But I thought you liked brown bread," I said.

Andrea nodded. "Lots better than white bread!"

We had been eating brown bread ever since our diet change over a year ago. Usually it was homemade, full bodied and rich with honey and whole wheat flour—and now and then made into our favorite—cinnamon swirl.

We all had agreed that we preferred even the store bought brown bread to white.

"But you won't eat it because the kids tease you?" I asked. I then realized that peer pressure was something to be reckoned with even in the first grade. I decided right then that the time to deal with this peer pressure was *now* — instead of waiting for the drug and alcohol peer pressure she will more than likely face in her teen years.

"No one else has brown bread!" Andrea said.

"Well," I said, thinking fast, "maybe you could do something about that. Maybe they just don't know how good it is. Remember when we read *Tom Sawyer*? Remember the part of the story about him whitewashing the fence?"

"And he made all the kids think it was lots of fun so they'd want to do it too and he wouldn't have to!" Andrea exclaimed.

I had thought at the time I read the story to her that *Tom Sawyer* wasn't exactly first grade level literature but Andrea had been intrigued by the illustration and had insisted on hearing it. Evidently this first grader had gotten the point. Andrea was off and running.

The next afternoon after school she reported that she had eaten her sandwich right in front of everyone and told them how good it tasted — just like on TV. I would have loved to have been a little mouse in the corner listening to *that* commercial!

Then the following day, besides reminding her lunch mates how good brown bread tasted, she told them how good it was for them. I hoped that didn't blow the selling campaign for her since "it's good for you" is not usually a prime selling point with kids — or adults either, for that matter.

On the third day in typical TV commercial style she attacked the rival product.

"What'd you say?" Tom asked, as Andrea related lunchtime happenings at the dinner table that evening. He settled back in his chair for a rerun.

"I asked Timmy Smith why he ate that plain old white bread. I said, 'It hasn't got any taste and it hasn't got vitamins and stuff that's good for you like brown bread has.'" She paused and giggled then picked up her napkin. "I said, 'You might as well eat your paper napkin!'"

Not all the first graders switched to brown bread, but Andrea did happily report converts from time to time throughout that year. Now she was no longer the only one with brown bread sandwiches — not that it mattered to her anymore. Andrea had already taken a very admirable step toward overcoming peer pressure! We were so pleased with her!

It also felt good to think that our little Darren had indirectly been instrumental in helping not only *our* family to eat more nutritiously — but perhaps some *other* families as well!

* * * * *

But then there was potty training. The only reason Darren's personal habits were not more trouble than they were was because all of the adults in charge of him were trained to see that he went to the bathroom at necessary intervals. However, spare clothing was kept at school and it was not an unusual occurrence for him to come home with a plastic bag of wet things. Darren simply had not taken on this responsibility. Whether it was that he *couldn't* or *wouldn't* no one knew. Nevertheless, I kept trying — even though the doctor said microcephalics could never be potty trained. So when I discovered a book *Toilet Training in Less Than a Day* by Nathan Azrin, I decided to give it another try.

The book related in quite explicit detail, though in child language, just exactly what going to the potty was all about. Andrea declined to sit in on reading sessions of that wonderful little volume but Darren listened with fascination as I read it to him on several successive days as the book instructed. Then I set out to help him put all of that information into practice.

The method was to have the child sit on the potty *all day*. Whenever he performed acceptably, he was to be rewarded.

On one of Darren's "at home" days, I settled him in the kitchen on the portable potty chair with toys to keep him occupied. There was plenty in the kitchen to keep me busy. I optimistically had some rewards ready—tidbits of dried fruit—which were as much of a treat to Darren as candy would have been to most children.

All day! Well it might work...*if* I could keep him there. After all he *was* on the potty so whatever happened would happen on the potty. He couldn't help but be successful...could he?

Darren sat on the potty and played contentedly for a surprisingly long time. Nothing happened, however, to merit a reward. I was working at the counter and wondering how long it was going to take when suddenly I was startled with something warm and wet on the back of my leg. After peeling myself off the ceiling, I hastily directed him back to the potty where he finished his performance. It was sort of a success. I gave him a couple raisins, hoping he had gotten the idea of what was expected of him and had him help clean up the part of his performance that was not a success, reminding him all the while that next time he should put it *all* in the potty.

It turned out to be a very long day. Followed by three more long days—contrary to what the book promised—but it worked! Darren still wet the bed at night, but days were no longer a problem. What amazing progress...once more Darren had proved all the doctors wrong and done "the impossible!"

CHAPTER 24

Off to See the Wizard

That year the whole city of Stanton was shaken by the senseless murder of three innocent teenage boys who were slaughtered gangland style as they were working to help to remodel a downtown building. That infamous day came to be known as "Black Sunday" and it was to have a far-reaching effect on our family because two of the boys were sons of Tom's employer and the other the son of a fellow employee. A blanket of despair settled on the firm itself from which it never recovered. Within months the company had gone bankrupt, and Tom found himself out of work.

Whatever would become of us? After this happened then came the "big 80's recession," so jobs were not easy to find for anyone, even professionals as well qualified and experienced as Tom. Horror stories had already been circulating of talented, educated people going for months or even years without jobs, having to draw unemployment compensation or working at low paying jobs for which they were over-qualified.

We were particularly concerned as to what all this would mean for Darren. The special training at P.A.C., the vitamin and mineral supplements, the specialists we consulted from time to time, our rainbow chasing—would all that have to go? Would we have to quit searching for answers?

Tom immediately began his job search in earnest. By Christmas he had sent out thirty resumés to firms in both the city and also some distant places. We were hoping something would turn up so we wouldn't have to move but we were preparing ourselves for any change that might have to be made. The job market definitely was not good and we would have to go where the job was.

* * * * *

The first of the year arrived without the threat of pending starvation at least. While no solid job offers had turned up, Tom had lined up some freelance work that would tide us over for a while. He set up an office in the guest room.

One afternoon he came home from a job with a stack of books.

"I just heard about something I think we ought to look into," he announced as he passed through the family room where I was sewing.

"What's that?" I asked.

"Metaphysics."

"What's that?" I asked again, sounding like a broken record.

"I don't know yet exactly but I"m going to check it out. Got to talking with some people who are into it." It seems that it was through this conversation he learned about health and past life psychic readings as guides to health and wholeness. One could have a reading done for fifteen dollars. The only information the reader needed was the location of the person at the time of the reading. Tom was skeptical but intrigued and requested a reading on Darren. Maybe it was just a wild goose chase but what if there was something to it? Wouldn't it be worth fifteen dollars to find out?

When Tom saw the transcript of Darren's reading, his heart began to pound. The reading covered physical, mental, emotional and spiritual aspects of Darren's life with bone-chilling accuracy—it was like a psychic x-ray. The "reading" pointed out that the back of his eyes were atrophied and scarred and his inner ear channels were smaller than normal ... *exactly* what the doctors had discovered. How could the psychics know all this with the little information they had been given—without even seeing Darren?

We decided to have a reading done on Tom's mother. Recently widowed, she was deteriorating both mentally and physically before our very eyes and we were very concerned. Again the accuracy of the reading was startling and described the same conditions the medical doctors had—kidney and bladder problems, high blood pressure, extreme loneliness and depression. Based on that reading, we helped her make some changes in her life which over time brought about noticeable improvement.

After these two readings our interest in metaphysics went beyond mere curiosity. This must be for real—we had to learn more!

Tom joined the School of Metaphysics, a small group that met in a house on the north side of town. For the next six months or so, when he wasn't working, he was pouring over that stack of books or taking classes across town.

The classes were part of the program at The Keegan Institute, which according to a brochure Tom brought home was dedicated to the study of the philosophy of metaphysics and had branches all over the country.

As to metaphysics, the dictionary defined it as a branch of philosophy that deals with the nature of existence, truth and knowledge—but that didn't describe what went on at the Institute.

Mostly it was a continuation of the healing classes we had taken in Minneapolis, with discussions and demonstrations on getting in touch with the powers—both within and without—by which a person may be brought to wholeness of mind and body. Energy auras, visions and dreams, mind control, out-of-body experiences and spirit guides were of great importance. Once a week the group met for study, meditation and prayer and there were daily readings, mind exercises, prayers and mantras to repeat. The study material, which included the Bible, covered methods of increasing "Christ-consciousness" to bring disciples to higher and higher levels of consciousness until they ultimately became not only god-like, but gods with supernatural powers to bring help and healing to a troubled world!

Would this put us in control of our own destiny, Darren's destiny, anyone's destiny? What kind of intelligence does it take to become a god? Can anyone decide to become a god and determine destinies? Who determined that Darren be born as he was and born into our family? Could only smart intellectuals become god-like or gods — perhaps only those with high self-esteem, high self-worth or self-love? With so many self-claimed, intellectual gods who would get the credit, the glory?

While we realized this was "weird stuff", the primary goals of the Institute were to bring people to a knowledge of truth that would lead to good health, happiness and fulfillment. Who could argue with that? Bible verses were scattered throughout their literature, which even mentioned Christ, so if some things seemed "weird," at least they must be a good kind of weird. The Bible told about strange things that couldn't be explained, didn't it?

When Tom learned that Doan Keegan — the founder of the Institute — was going to be in town, he made an appointment for a consultation with Darren.

Doan Keegan had the special gift of mind reading — a capacity he had been born with. The story went that as a young child he came to realize that he knew what other people were thinking before they even spoke. This became a real problem when he was with a group of people and he would be bombarded with their thoughts. Somehow, he learned to control his reception of the thoughts and had dedicated his life to using his gift to help others.

As it turned out, Tom had some business out of town the day of the appointment so I was the one to take Darren for an audience with the Great One.

By this time consultations were not new to Darren, but as always, I explained to him just what we were going to do. He took it all in, nodding gravely.

We arrived at the Institute and Darren walked sedately beside me as we approached the house, holding my hand quietly until I opened the door. Then suddenly something seemed to go haywire. Without warning, he jerked his hand free and headed back to the car. I managed to grab him, turn him around, pull him inside and shut the door — but not without a struggle.

The waiting room was occupied by several people who watched with amusement as I tried to settle Darren down. He crawled onto the bottom shelf of an open built-in bookcase — creating a space for himself with a lot of thumping and shuffling that included pushing the books at the other end out on the floor. I hauled him out of there and while I was replacing the books with one hand and holding on to him with the other, he started whining and trying to climb to the top of the bookcase like a monkey. By now the spectators were looking less than amused, and I decided to take Darren outside and begin all over again.

In the car once more I repeated my lecture on what he could expect and how he was to behave. Again he nodded gravely...not at all the little hellion I had just led from the house.

Back again at the door, Darren planted his feet at the threshold and I had to drag him in as he whined in protest. A rumpled heavy-set man with a florid complexion appeared for a moment in the hallway that led from the waiting room. He glanced at Darren and me for a moment — looking a bit annoyed I thought — and then disappeared back down the hall. Since the same people were still in the waiting room, I figured we would have a lengthy wait. There being no receptionist to check in with, I murmured to the world in general that we would be back in a while and took Darren for a walk around the block.

He was a model child until I again tried to herd him into the house. This time he put up such a howl that I immediately hauled him back outside and shut the door, but I did have time to notice that only one person remained in the waiting room. We took another stroll around the block, Darren hopping contentedly along, chattering and me responding absent mindedly and debating whether to go back again—or just forget the whole thing and go home.

Thinking maybe the third time would be the charm, I tried going back in again, but this time he began to howl and dragged his feet. At least the waiting room was empty this time so I started digging in my purse for something to distract Darren when the rumpled man appeared in the hall doorway, inquired as to whether I was Mrs. Jones and introduced himself as Doan Keegan.

This was Doan Keegan?! He certainly didn't fit my idea of the learned grand guru of Keegan Institute. I hoped my shock wasn't too evident.

He led us down the hall into a room that apparently served as his office. While apologizing for Darren's disruptive behavior, I sat down on a chair in front of the desk where Mr. Keegan had taken his place and tried to settle Darren on my lap.

"Yes, I would expect that he did not want to come here today," he said, finally. "He knows he is going to be found out."

"Found out?"

"I'll explain later," he said and amiably turned his attention to Darren.

For the next fifteen or twenty minutes I had the feeling that I was witnessing a battle of sorts. Darren stubbornly resisted all of Mr. Keegan's attempts to be friends and would not even look at him, but kept his head down, looking furtively out of the corner of one eye and then the other. When the encounter had ended, I wasn't quite sure who had won, though Mr. Keegan seemed to think he had. He suggested that I come back that evening by myself for the answer to the "being found out" question and to discuss his recommendations for Darren.

I would have been more comfortable having Tom come along for the consultation with Mr. Keegan but he was exhausted after his business trip and, besides that, we didn't want to spend money on a baby sitter.

The waiting room was quite well filled when I arrived at the Institute that evening. I scanned the bookshelves for something to pass the time and settled on a booklet on dream therapy — interpreting dreams according to Biblical symbols in order to gain insight for solving problems. I found it to be fascinating reading. This was something I would like to pursue further — if only I could ever remember what I had dreamed. But there was help for that too, according to the booklet.

By the time Mr. Keegan summoned me into the inner sanctum, I felt as though I had been in another world so I was totally unprepared for what he had to tell me.

"Your son, Mrs. Jones, is not retarded. In fact, he borders on being a genius," he said as though there was no question in his mind whatsoever that what he was saying was true.

"But...but...," I could only stammer.

"Yes, I know about the brain damage and all the rest, but he is not retarded. That is why he did not want to come here. He knew he would be found out. He didn't want me to tell you. That is why he was so uncooperative. He knew I could read his thoughts. He has a brilliant mind, but he does not want to use it. If he seems to be retarded, it is because you have made him so. You have allowed, perhaps even encouraged, him to avoid using that brilliant mind of his. You have overprotected him, not allowing him to be himself. You have accepted the idea that he is retarded and he is pleased to go along with you."

Waves of emotion swept over me. Darren not retarded! Could it be true? And I was the cause of his problems?

"Yes, you are wondering if you can believe what I am saying," Mr. Keegan said, gazing at me steadily, "but you will discover that it is true. You must release your son from the negative influences you have been inflicting upon him. Your task now is to search for ways to help him achieve his full potential."

He had more to say regarding ways in which the Institute would help in this search he spoke of but I was unable to take it in. Apparently he knew that though — was he *really* reading my mind? — for suddenly I realized that the consultation was over. I didn't remember any exchange of farewells. In a daze, I stumbled across the waiting room and out into the darkness.

I headed the car toward home trying to put what he had told me into some kind of perspective. Could I believe that it was true, that Darren was not retarded? If I did, then would I have to take responsibility for making him like he was?

Suddenly it was more than I could deal with. My breath was coming in great, heaving sobs. I pulled over to the curb, turned off the motor and gave in to the hysteria that was enveloping me. I sat there for perhaps fifteen minutes, bent over the steering wheel, my head on my arms, uncontrollably weeping tears of frustration and anger. I wanted to strike out at somebody. Everything that Darren and all of us as a family had been through — it was surely not *my* fault! I hadn't accepted what the specialists had told us from the very beginning! I hadn't been a negative influence! I had searched and worked and suffered and sacrificed!

Finally the hysteria was spent, if not the frustration and anger. I dried my tears, noticing for the first time that I had stopped in front of a busy convenience store and people were looking at me curiously. I was too upset to care.

When I arrived home, Tom was asleep on the sofa, a book lying open facedown on his chest. He roused when I crossed the room to hang my coat in the closet, and when he saw me he sat up abruptly, suddenly wide awake.

"What happened?" he asked with some alarm in his voice, sensing that something was wrong.

"He said Darren isn't retarded and may be a genius and his problems are all my fault!" I blurted out, sitting down beside Tom on the sofa.

"What?"

"Yeah," I said, knowing he had heard perfectly well what I had said, but needed time to digest it. "I don't know how to deal with that!" I said in a choking voice.

After a long silence, Tom said softly, "Neither do I... but it's not your fault!" he added firmly.

I could only whisper through my tears, "Thanks!"

"Isn't it strange," Tom said, breaking another long silence, "that this is the most positive thing anyone has ever said about Darren and look at us!"

"I guess we don't really believe it's true."

"But what if it is?"

We mulled the question over for a while. Could Darren have a genius understanding of love, enough to feel spiritually uncomfortable in the metaphysical surroundings? Could he see an evil spiritual side? Could this be the genius Doan Keegan was talking about? We would have to wait and see.

After all Doan Keegan was not God. He didn't know everything.

On my way to bed I looked in on Andrea and Darren as I always did. I lingered at Darren's bedside searching his pinched little face in the dim light from the hallway, wondering...if only I could believe what Mr. Keegan had said, perhaps I could somehow bear the guilt of being the cause of his problems.

CHAPTER 25

Hills and Valleys at Five

That spring Darren turned five. We celebrated the occasion with a fire truck party...his idea. All the neighborhood kids were invited and on the invitation they were told to bring a raincoat.

Tom constructed an apartment village—as he called it—in our backyard, by fastening big cardboard appliance boxes together, cutting out windows and doors and creating doorways between the apartments. When the kids arrived for the party, they were given small boxes of crayons, which were put to use coloring flames on the buildings.

This done, they were herded to Andrea's bedroom which had been turned into a giant spider web made of string woven over, under, around and through all the furnishings in the room again and again. At the door were the ends of the string, each one tied to a clothespin with the name of a child written on it. The children were each to take the clothespin with their name on it and start winding the string around it. Eventually, with much crawling and reaching and untangling—to say nothing of tussling, squealing, shouting and laughing—each one came to his prize...a squirt gun that had been concealed under or inside of something at the end of each string.

Once the children had found their squirt gun, we instructed them to get back outside because the apartment village was on fire—and it was their job to put it out! The kids were only too happy to oblige! They tossed on their raincoats, filled their squirt guns from the bucket of water that stood handy and got to work! Some kids crawled inside the boxes, wanting to be squirted and some wanted to be the firemen and do the squirting. Everyone was having a grand time, which probably could have continued for the rest of the afternoon.

In the middle of this free-for-all, however, a real fire truck with its siren blowing and lights flashing pulled up in front of our house. A fireman jumped off the truck and came running to offer his help. All this, of course, had been prearranged. Whether or not it's always so easy to get a visit from the fire department just for fun we didn't know, but we sure were grateful.

When the make believe fire was put out to the satisfaction of everyone the kids looked the fire truck over close up and the birthday boy got to sit in the driver's seat of the truck and pull the cord for the siren.

The cake I had baked was a miniature fire engine to continue the theme. No one remembers what kind of cake other than it was made with honey instead of sugar and it was covered with a strawberry glaze over cream cheese icing. Sesame seeds pressed into the icing made headlights and long, fat pretzels served as hoses. There were even firemen's boots made from prune skins lined up on the running board. The cake and the entire party were a complete success!

* * * * *

Due to financial constraints, we spent that summer conservatively. Our vacation was a week at the home of Tom's parents during the last week in July.

Even after a whole year, Darren still adored the Big Wheel we got him for his fourth birthday and wanted to take it with him to Grandpa and Grandma's. We decided he could get along without it for a week since there would be plenty of other things to do and persuaded him to leave the Big Wheel at home.

Boy were we wrong! Andrea was soon happily occupied with a half dozen different projects but Darren didn't want to do *anything* except ride the Big Wheel that wasn't there.

To help distract him, I took him along to a neighborhood garage sale.

"You don't happen to have anything with wheels, do you?" I quietly asked the cashier over Darren's head.

"Just that old broken bike over there," she said, nodding toward the back of the garage.

At the word "bike" Darren came alive. "I want a bike, Mom!" he shouted, jumping up and down.

"Well I don't think you can ride a two wheel bike," I said, but we went over to look anyway.

It was a little yellow bicycle—I had never seen one so small. One pedal was missing, but otherwise it was in pretty good shape.

"I want it, Mom!" he insisted, plunking himself down on the seat. Actually, it was just his size—his feet rested neatly on the ground.

"But you don't know how to ride a two wheeler yet," I objected.

"I do too!" he announced and pushed himself forward with his feet to prove it.

I had to concede that his method would work very nicely with this bicycle that had only one pedal anyway.

"How much?" I asked the lady in charge.

"Oh, how about a dollar?"

"We"ll take it!"

Darren sat contentedly on the little bicycle pushing it one step forward then one step back while I finished browsing and made some other purchases.

As for the bicycle—I couldn't have spent a dollar better! Darren spent nearly all his waking hours the rest of our vacation on his little yellow bicycle going back and forth on the sidewalk in front of the house — step, step, step. We had to bribe and cajole to get him to come in for meals and more than once Tom carried him in bodily. More than once I was tempted to just give him a sack lunch and let it go at that.

Tom took off the one pedal which was only in the way considering Darren's method of riding. As long as he was happy, who cared whether he pedaled it or not! It had only been within the last year that Andrea had finally learned to ride her bike without training wheels. Genius or not, we weren't expecting more than that from her little brother.

When it came time to go home, we tried to persuade Darren to leave the bicycle at Grandpa and Grandma's so he would have something to play with the next time he came for a visit. After all, he had his Big Wheel to ride at home.

No way! Darren wanted to take his bike home!

Remembering our earlier decision that hadn't turned out so well, Tom shrugged. "Why fight it?" he said with resignation and loaded Darren's newest treasure into the back of the station wagon on top of the suitcases.

Darren was back on his bike as soon as we got home. The sidewalk in front of our house sloped gently downward to the end of the block which made bicycle riding even more fun at home than at Grandpa and Grandma's house.

Several days after we got home, I was doing some outside work when I heard a cry of glee from the bicyclist.

"Hey! Look! I"m balancing!" he yelled.

Balancing! First of all, I didn't realize he even knew that word! And then *doing* it? But there he was, sailing down the sidewalk on two wheels, both feet high off the ground. It looked like Darren was ready for pedals!

Tom and Darren went to the bicycle shop that afternoon and got pedals for the little yellow bike and the next thing we knew, Darren was expertly pedaling up and down the sidewalk just as though he'd been riding a two wheeler all his life.

Our apologies, Mr. Keegan! Maybe you were right after all! Darren's method of separating the task by first learning to balance and then learning to pedal was actually better than the old tried and true training wheels method!

It was exhausting for us to try to figure out what the right thing to do was as far as Darren was concerned. Since the consultation with Doan Keegan, I was constantly evaluating everything I did, trying to determine if I was really not allowing him to develop on his own. Sometimes I would decide that I was being too strict and overbearing and would back off. Then I would decide I was being too easy and would go back to being more strict again.

As fall approached we felt it was time to make a change in Darren's schooling. Probably influenced by Mr. Keegan's evaluation to some extent, we felt a need to get him into a more normal school environment and finally decided to take him out of P.A.C. and enroll him in the public school special education program right in our own neighborhood. Of course, economic considerations entered into this decision also.

We were feeling very good about this until the call from the school principal's office. Upon reviewing Darren's records, the powers-that-be felt that our child would be better off placed in the facility for handicapped children on the other side of town.

A wave of apprehension swept over me and I began to object, but from the response at the other end of the line, I sensed that it was all settled. They weren't asking, they were *telling*. Each day a taxi driver would come directly to our house. Darren would be driven by taxi to Cromwell, the special school. A free taxi ride was part of the package of being sent to a school so far from home!

I had heard about Cromwell at P.A.C. It had been in operation for many years, serving as a community center for people with all kinds of needs and was well respected for its work with the handicapped. Nevertheless, I couldn't shake the feeling of apprehension...or perhaps it was resentment.

I drove Darren to Cromwell myself the first day of school. I couldn't imagine sending any five year old off across town all by himself for the first time in a taxi to a strange new school and certainly not Darren. In the first place, he was definitely not happy with this change in his school situation. He had been looking forward to going to school with Andrea this year. All the way, while he fidgeted worriedly on the seat beside me, I carried on an overly cheerful, mostly one sided, conversation about all the nice things that would be going on at the new school.

After nearly a half hour drive, we arrived. This was obviously an older part of town and the neighborhood was beginning to deteriorate, but the Cromwell property—a huge old mansion—was neatly kept. Behind the house I could see a fenced-in yard with play equipment.

A little girl in a wheelchair propelling herself up a ramp at one end of the house distracted Darren from his own troubles as we got out of the car and he walked quite willingly beside me up the front steps and into the house.

We entered a reception hall and from a directory beside the door found our way to the kindergarten room for disabled children—which perhaps in grander, long ago days had been a ballroom. Now somewhere between forty and fifty little children milled noisily about as several adults attempted to look after them. A tall, energetic young woman greeted us and after determining just who Darren was, she took him by the hand and led him over to one of the shepherds. I sensed that my presence was no longer needed or desired.

"I'll be back at noon," I called. Darren looked back but made no response, evidently resigned to his fate for the time being.

When I returned at noon, the room was in the same state of confusion as when I had left. I hoped it hadn't been like that the entire morning but wouldn't have been surprised if it had been. I realized, however, that I had been prejudiced against Cromwell from the beginning, simply because of the circumstances of Darren's having to go there. Still I didn't like the looks of the set up. I didn't see how any real learning could take place with all that hubbub. There were too many children and too much going on, even for a grand ballroom.

As we drove away from Cromwell, Darren huddled in his seat looking like a thunderstorm brewing. "No more school!" he declared.

He probably meant forever but I responded with false cheeriness. "Nope! Not until tomorrow." I could have added, "And then you get to ride to school in a taxi all by yourself!" But even I wasn't ready for that yet.

The next morning he went reluctantly into the taxi — after having been practically pried out of bed and hand fed to get enough breakfast into him to last until snack time at school.

Each morning thereafter got progressively worse.

Afternoons he played listlessly around the house except when he was teasing Muffin or picking a quarrel with Andrea. Never a hearty eater, now he hardly even picked at his food. He slept restlessly, tossing and turning and sometimes crying out in his sleep. I had no idea what was going on at school. He didn't want to talk about it. When anyone ventured to ask what he did at school, he would glumly reply, "Nothin…"

I waited it out for two weeks then put in a call to Cromwell. I talked with one of the teachers, who told me that they were all aware of Darren's misery and that he was being "quite uncooperative." They suggested that we give him a little more time to adjust. I didn't say so but I thought enough time had passed. I was tired of waiting and, knowing Darren, I didn't think more time would change anything. I felt the whole situation—the long taxi rides and the hyperactivity of the classroom—was simply more than he could handle. I didn't know what it took to reverse an official school ultimatum, but I decided it was time to find out.

As it turned out, all it took was a visit to the school principal by a distraught mother. (I would find out later that this success was only beginner's luck, but that's another chapter in the saga of "The Education of Darren Jones".) The principal graciously listened to my story and after a couple of telephone conversations in his inner office, he informed me that everything was set for Darren to attend the Special Ed class at Hoover Elementary—effective immediately!

"...Out came the sun and dried up all the rain..." Darren was a changed little boy when he found out that he didn't have to go back to Cromwell. The daily war to get him off to school ended.

He came home his second day at Hoover with a project for Dad. "You ought to come to school and help the teachers get a great big drill off the roof," he said.

A drill on the roof? What was going on at school?

"Well we had a *fire* drill at school today," Andrea said, wrinkling her nose in puzzlement.

Finally after a bit of questioning, we pieced the story together. The only kind of drill Darren knew about was the tool Tom used to make holes in wood. When the alarm sounded at school, he heard talk of a drill and everyone went outside and sure enough, up there on the roof was something that his unreliable eyes led him to imagine was an enormous drill. We explained that there is more than one kind of drill so he would understand during future drills, but it was a typical "Darrenism" like the fish-that-grew when we were at the lake.

So what about it, Mr. Keegan? Is he a genius with very bad eyes, or is he a kid with very bad eyes who has a great imagination for figuring out the world around him? In any case, it seemed that this Special Ed class was the right place for Darren and he went quite happily to school most mornings.

CHAPTER 26

Is the Answer in the Stars?

I could scarcely believe my ears when Tom came home from a consultation with a prospective client talking about astrology.

"But that's hocus pocus!" I objected.

"No, no, I"m not talking about horoscopes — the stuff you read in the newspapers and magazines — what you should do on a certain day if you're born under a certain sign," he explained. "But there's a man by the name of Clay Calder in Hamilton that famous people from all over the world come to for advice — like leaders in Washington, DC and worldly business executives. He has even been invited to the White House."

Advice. We certainly could use advice. Something that would help us know what direction we should take with Darren. Maybe something that would confirm what Mr. Keegan said. And long ago, we had said that we'd try anything, no matter how far out, as long as it wouldn't hurt Darren. We didn't see how this could hurt. So...

The first step in having an astrological reading done was to give the astrologer the place, date and time of birth of the subject. With this information he would construct charts on which he based his conclusions. On Mr. Calder's advice, we decided to have readings done on the whole family and Tom gave him the necessary information over the phone. After waiting two weeks we were summoned for a consultation at his home fifty miles away.

We sat mesmerized as this man told us all about ourselves, including some family background that we hadn't thought about for years. He went into the recent stresses of Tom's career with some detail and cautioned that within the next few months Tom would be entering into a "very positive cycle with new incentives and interests." He would need to take great care with financial interests to avoid losses and also he should avoid long distance travel. Mr. Calder observed that despite being a talented man with skills in many areas, employers tended not to realize or appreciate Tom's potential and it was likely that he would at last find his greatest success and fulfillment in a business of his own.

Nothing earth-shaking came up in the charts on me, except they showed that I was the spiritual one in the family, which I had a little trouble believing. I would have said Tom was the spiritual one, though neither of us rated very high in my opinion.

Andrea, the charts said, displayed a great deal of talent in art, music and writing, as well as in business — no surprise, really — and mentioned a kidney infection she had had when she was two years old that had left scar tissue. No ill effects were anticipated from this in later life as long as she followed "reasonable habits of healthful living." I made a mental note to impress upon Andrea the value of what we had learned in our nutrition forays on behalf of Darren and felt grateful, as well as a little smug, for what had been accomplished in that direction.

Then, at last, the focus was on Darren. "Now as to your daughter, Martha..." Mr. Calder began.

"He's not our daughter...and his name is Darren," Tom interrupted.

Mr. Calder shrugged off the interruption as though it was of no consequence and proceeded to give an otherwise accurate rundown of Darren's life to date.

His chart showed stress every year until age twenty which Mr. Calder said could indicate that the birth problems need not be permanent. Through initiative and persistent effort on our part good progress could be made. The next year was particularly favorable for health and the next three years for psychic healing. He suggested that we investigate this course as well as encourage artistic and musical appreciation and development. These interests would be strengths that would keep him from undesirable peer influence. Throughout his life he must avoid horses and motorcycles. Either of these could be very dangerous.

In addition, Mr. Calder recommended that we contact a group on the west coast whose work sounded like something out of the Bible with talk about laying on of hands and prayer. He told us we could write and ask to have Darren's name put on their prayer list. Perhaps we would even want to consider taking him out there.

We left the Calder residence with a feeling of optimism. It was heartening to again hear some positive input with regard to Darren even though the astrology charts and Mr. Keegan's observations didn't exactly agree. Whatever questions we might have had about astrology, there seemed to be something more here than just hocus pocus.

As we drove home, we discussed contacting the prayer group Mr. Calder had mentioned. We thought it sounded legitimate and decided we would at least write and find out about it.

After driving several miles in silence, Tom mused, "I guess Calder's right about me — my work..."

I agreed. "That's what I"ve been telling you for years...your bosses don't appreciate you!"

"But I've never had a hankering to have my own business. The freelancing isn't too bad for a while, but I don't want a business of my own permanently."

"Not even if it would give you success and fulfillment like he said?"

"Depends on what he means by success and fulfillment. I like to put myself into my work and do it right but I don't want it to take up my whole life. I"ve seen lots of guys with their own businesses go that route—they end up with no time for family or other interests."

"If you could do anything you wanted to do what would that be?" I tossed out, still caught up in "success and fulfillment."

"Run an orphanage," Tom responded with scarcely a moment's hesitation.

"You're kidding, aren't you?" I said, looking at him, trying to decide if he was or not.

"Nope. That's what I would really like to do if I could do anything I wanted to do."

"I have an idea that would be more involvement than having your own business."

"Yeah, probably, but that would be different."

"And I suppose you'd expect me to help you."

"Sure!"

"What if I don't want to run an orphanage?"

"Well, maybe we could work out something. I'd still like to keep you around."

"Thanks!"

"No problem!" Tom turned his attention to traffic as we approached the freeway off ramp at our exit.

"You really would like to run an orphanage, wouldn't you?" I ventured after a moment.

"Yeah, I really would! But don't worry. I have no intention of doing so, much as I would like to. How would I support the family?"

That evening I wrote a letter to the prayer group on the west coast. I told them as much as I thought necessary about Darren and asked what we had to do to have his name put on their prayer list. A couple of weeks later a handwritten reply came saying that Darren's name had been put on their prayer list. Surprisingly there was no plea for money and that was the last we ever heard from them. We puzzled over the connection of this group to astrology. Somehow astrology and healing by prayer just didn't go together in our minds, but we couldn't say why.

We also decided to follow up on the advice the astrology readings had given us with regard to music for Darren. He never had shown much interest in music, except for occasionally banging on the piano—usually when Andrea wanted to practice her lesson. Now I indulged in fantasies of our little boy becoming a musical prodigy. But what instrument? This called for some expert help.

One Saturday morning the four of us paid a visit to the big music store downtown where we made the acquaintance of Mr. Henry. He talked with us for a few minutes, drawing Darren comfortably into the conversation, then gave a demonstration of some of the instruments on display, letting both Andrea and Darren handle them and try them out.

It was soon obvious that a wind instrument was not within Darren's capabilities because of the malformation of his teeth due to his small head. We had thought probably drums would appeal to him but he didn't seem particularly interested and I admit I was glad. Drums did not fit in with my child prodigy fantasies. Mr. Henry was suggesting that perhaps piano would be the best solution as a beginning instrument when we came to a display of violins.

Suddenly Darren's eyes lit up. "That!" he said, pointing.

We looked questioningly at Mr. Henry. We couldn't imagine Darren even being interested in the violin, much less learning to play one.

Mr. Henry chuckled. "Sometimes they know what they can handle," he said, "even two year olds have been taught how to play the violin." He took a small one out of the showcase and let Darren try it.

Darren was entranced, even though he produced nothing but squawks and squeaks. We decided to give violin a try and signed up for a package deal to rent the instrument with six weeks of lessons with Mr. Henry.

Darren and Mr. Henry had a fun time. Mr. Henry was wonderful with children and soon had Darren *looking* very good as he ran the bow across the strings. But *sounding* good never did happen. Darren did not have the fine motor dexterity to do the fingering required to play the violin and, not surprisingly, he didn't think it was any fun to practice.

Mr. Henry's philosophy regarding children's learning music was simple—bribery. Children have to be rewarded to practice because they don't see the need for it—they don't connect being able to play well with practicing.

With Darren, after the novelty had worn off, nothing could interest him in practicing and the violin lessons petered out. Dreams of our son, the musician, had to be put on hold. Maybe we could try again in a few years.

CHAPTER 27

But You're Not Supposed to Read!

Darren's teacher during his second year in Hoover Special Ed was Mrs. Moore—a quiet, unimpressive appearing lady—who nevertheless knew her business, we were to discover that year. Right from the start, Darren was bringing home worksheets that looked like real schoolwork. Most of them, by the time he had finished with them were pretty messy, but it did appear that he was actually making some progress at last in following directions and in eye/hand coordination.

Little did we know! One cold, windy day in March, Darren came home with a book, the same primer Andrea had had when she was in first grade. He pointed solemnly to a note from Mrs. Moore that was clipped to the book. "Please have Darren read pages 1 through 4" the note read in neat teacher manuscript.

"Oh come *on* lady!" I thought. Maybe Darren had made some progress but I knew good and well that he couldn't *read!*

But Darren already had his nose to page one—and to my astonishment—he read every word of a story about a little black dog and a red ball! Not without some stumbling and long pauses, but he *read it!* And I started crying. (I still cry when I tell this story.)

Darren looked up from his book in alarm. "Mom, why are you crying?"

I hugged him tightly. "Oh, I'm so happy and pleased with you!" I said, trying not to sound teary.

"Yeah," Darren said in a satisfied tone.

Andrea arrived home just then.

"Hey, you wanna hear me read?" Darren greeted her. Without waiting for an answer, he again put his nose to the book and began plowing through the story.

Andrea, shrugging off her coat, stood peering over his shoulder. "Oh, I remember that," she interrupted. "That's good, Darren! But I can't see the pictures. Do you have to stick your whole head right in the book?"

"Just a minute!" he said testily. After he had labored through all four pages, he closed the book. "There!" he said, handing it to Andrea to look for herself and went off to see what was in the kitchen for a snack.

Tom was out delivering some work to a client that afternoon and I could hardly wait for him to return. When I heard him drive in, I called Darren. He came plodding up the stairs from the family room.

"Dad's home," I said. "Get your book so you can read for him."

Darren galloped into the living room and returned empty handed just as Tom came in the door. "Hi, Dad!" he said, giving him a bear hug. "You wanna hear me read?"

"I sure do!" Tom responded, giving me a questioning look over Darren's head.

"He can!" I choked out, barely able to hold back my tears.

After a brief mad search for the book—it was under some papers in the living room—Darren read again! And Dad's eyes looked a little misty too when the story was finished.

"That's great, Darren!" Tom said hugging him.

"Yeah!" he said. In contrast to his casual acceptance of this new skill he'd learned, we were finding it hard to contain our elation! Our little boy—who even on a "good" day couldn't count beyond ten, didn't know the names of colors...in fact we weren't sure that he even *saw* color—was reading! Admittedly, it was with stumbling and hesitation, but he *was* reading! Is this the little boy who could...when doctors said he couldn't? What was next?

Were we on the right track at last? Was it just a coincidence that things seemed to be improving for Darren or did it have something to do with the astrology and the prayer group and nutrition and everything? Though we didn't fully understand it, we couldn't explain it away.

"Is it...God?" I asked Tom as we mulled it all over that evening after the kids had gone to bed.

"I guess it has to be," Tom said slowly.

"Why do you say 'has to be'?"

"Because according to what I"ve been studying, God is in everything and everything is God. Even people... maybe we can be a god. I wonder about that though."

"If I were God, I wouldn't want to be connected with some of the terrible things that go on."

"I guess that's what bothers me. Still, the people who are into this want to do good. Basically they're good people trying to make the world a better place."

"And there is this...this Power...whatever it is... that seems to be working..."

"Some of the time anyway," Tom interrupted. "You know it sounds good—everyone doing all kinds of wonderful, miraculous things. But when I get to thinking about it, it's scary! Suppose we could work miracles. What if my miracle conflicts with yours? How does anyone know if what he thinks would be a good thing...really would be? It's probably best to let God do the miracles."

"Well, I'm willing to accept a miracle. No questions asked."

"Oh, I'll take a miracle, all right! And maybe that's what we've got!"

Whatever we wanted to call it, it was joyful beyond words to see Darren making such wonderful progress — progress we had been repeatedly assured he would never attain!

CHAPTER 28

Where Are All the Friends?

Just when we had decided that nothing was ever going to come of the countless resumes Tom had sent out, an attractive offer came from a company in Manning, a small town about fifty miles from Stanton. Having some concern about the educational options for Darren in this smaller city, we made an appointment with the superintendent of schools in Manning and spent over an hour questioning him in regard to the programs available for Darren. We came away confident that Darren would be provided with whatever he needed in education. "We must provide the least restrictive environment for his development," the superintendent reassured us, "it's 'the law'."

Little did we know about the workings of "the law"! Be that as it may, Tom accepted the position.

Without a great deal of fanfare, we sold our house before school was out and bought an attractive split level in a pleasant neighborhood in Manning.

But Andrea and Darren were having second thoughts about moving.

"I'll miss my friends!" Andrea confided tearfully one night at bedtime. "What'll we do without Cathy and all the other friends we had in the neighborhood?"

Taking up the refrain, Darren muttered gloomily, "No more Cathy! No more friends!"

I had wondered the same thing myself. But there would be new friends in Manning. "I'll bet there are lots of kids to play with there, just like there are here," I assured them both.

We moved in the middle of June. The day we arrived Andrea and Darren took a walk around the neighborhood and returned to report that they had seen some children out playing down at the other end of the block.

"But they just looked at us like we were creatures from outer space!" Andrea said. "They didn't even say hello. I don't think they want to be friends!"

"No friends..." Darren said mournfully, shaking his head in hopelessness.

"Oh, they"ll come around," Tom consoled. "I'll get the swing set up first thing."

We all pitched in to try to make the yard inviting enough to lure any child, no matter how shy or unfriendly — a swing set, a tire swing, a roomy sandbox with digging toys, and, in a tree with sturdy low branches, a little ladder that led up to a platform in the tree. But all to no avail.

"Mom, where are all the friends?" Darren asked after days of no one but me to play with.

He sounded so forlorn I felt like crying. I had run out of optimistic answers. What can we do to bring friends to Darren? Is there any hope? Will this new neighborhood ever accept and relate to our handicapped child?

Darren searched my worried face and then said comfortingly, "It's all right, Mom. They"ll come."

* * * * *

"Mom! There's going to be a parade! A Crazy Days parade—whatever that is," Andrea announced as she brought in the mail one day. She waved our first issue of the *Manning Courier* in front of me.

I learned upon scanning the newspaper that Crazy Days was a big summertime sale with a carnival atmosphere held downtown on the square.

There seemed to be no doubt in Andrea's mind that the Jones kids would be in the parade which was the day after tomorrow.

Well, why not? I decided. There was still settling in to do, but this would be fun and probably a chance to get acquainted with other kids. The settling in could wait. Darren and Andrea went on a scouting mission upstairs to locate our box of costume makings.

A clown outfit that Andrea had worn for Halloween a couple of years ago caught Darren's fancy as soon as the box was opened. After considerable discussion, we concluded that two clowns would be better than one, so I stitched up an outfit for Andrea from some colorful old curtains. As I was finishing that, Andrea picked up a length of leftover ruffle and tried it on Muffin. Three clowns would be even better than two—especially if one was a dog—so Andrea whipped up an outfit for Muffin...a ruffle and a pointed hat with a red pompom.

One thing led to another. When the parade made its way around the square, Andrea was on skates. In one hand was a fishing pole from which several hot dogs dangled a couple of feet ahead of her. In the other hand was Muffin's leash. Muffin was chasing after the hot dogs and sometimes grabbing one and at the same time pulling Andrea along on her skates. The only glitch turned out to be that before the parade was over, Muffin had had her fill of hot dogs and Andrea had to skate under her own power.

Happily, the Jones clowns won second prize. (Some thought it should have been first!) The prize was a three-dollar certificate from the dime store, which we cashed in on the way home. Andrea got a puzzle, Darren a little car and Muffin a rubber bone. Their picture, along with the other prizewinners, appeared in the *Courier* the following week.

It was probably the picture in the paper that finally brought some neighborhood children to our door, among them Eddie Eldridge.

Eddie was younger than Darren, but a half a head taller and of sturdier build and inclined to think because he was the biggest, he was the boss. Darren, of course, didn't see it that way and was not above saying so. Nevertheless, he was a playmate for Darren, even though they sometimes had their differences.

Though we had joined the church in Stanton, we were by no means outstanding "pillars-of-the-church" sort of members. If it fit in with our plans for the day, we went to church. If not, well...

However, our first Sunday in Manning found us going to church. Admittedly, our motivation was two-fold — we figured getting involved in a church would help us get acquainted more quickly in the community.

Due to a misunderstanding as to the time services began, we arrived too late for church, but just in time for Sunday School. A kindly, elderly gentlemen ushered Darren and Andrea off to their appropriate places. At least we hoped that wherever he was taking Darren would be appropriate. One never really knew.

We found ourselves in a lively class of eight or ten other couples about our age. It was a comfortable group with a lot of class participation — mixed in with some casual talk too. We felt quite at home and were glad we had come.

After class, our classmates informed us that Fellowship Hour followed Sunday School. Then they led us into a large room fragrant with coffee where people of all ages were milling around or sitting in little groups talking, sipping coffee and nibbling the refreshments set out at one end of the room.

Apparently, this was where families were reunited after Sunday School and all the church members socialized. We spotted Darren clinging to the hand of a slender teenage girl and peering around with a worried look. He brightened considerably when we came into his range of view, and he quickly let go of the girl's hand and grabbed mine. In a minute Andrea came in chattering happily with some girls her age. She gave us a casual wave from across the room and went on chattering.

We visited with several couples and by the time Fellowship Hour broke up we felt we had made some new friends.

We became regular attendees at Sunday School. The class was definitely unstructured—we seemed to be working our way through the Gospel of John, but no one was in any hurry and one little verse or phrase could send us off into an involved and often heart searching discussion. Sharon Rhodes, our teacher, was about our age and seemed to be pretty knowledgeable in the Bible and well prepared for our study, but she encouraged us to dig and delve into the Bible ourselves too.

In the course of class discussion one Sunday, we somehow got off on the Old Testament story of Daniel, his three friends and their brave stand in regard to the food their captors provided. This sparked some remarks from me about our experiment and the benefits of proper nutrition in our search for answers to Darren's problems.

During Fellowship Hour that Sunday, Marcie Bell—one of our Sunday School classmates—approached me with a purposeful look in her eye.

"Do you by any chance have any words of wisdom on nutrition for 'other problems'?" she asked.

"Well, that depends on what 'other problems' you have in mind," I replied.

"Female!" she whispered in a low and desperate tone. She told me that for years her menstrual periods had been accompanied with such pain and heavy bleeding that she would have to go to bed and sometimes even to the hospital. Now, in spite of medication and two D&Cs, they were getting worse, and the doctor was advising a hysterectomy as her only hope. "But I don't want surgery!" she said, finishing her tale of woe.

As Marcie was talking, I remembered an article in the Prevention Magazine that I'd received just that past week. I only scanned the article, but I had noticed that it gave a regimen of vitamins and minerals for problems such as Marcie's. I suggested she borrow the magazine from me, read the article and see if it could help her.

Although she was a bit skeptical, Marcie showed up on our doorstep Monday morning to borrow the magazine. She was full of questions for me. Did I think this would really work? And wasn't there a danger of overdosing on vitamins? I suggested that she check with her doctor. When she did so, the doctor's response was that it wouldn't hurt to try the regimen.

So Marcie went on the vitamin and mineral therapy. I asked her after a couple of weeks how things were going. She replied unenthusiastically that maybe it was helping a little. But a month later she called early one morning simply bubbling over.

"Joyce! It's working! It's working!" she told me with elation. "Only a few little cramps this month and no hemorrhaging! I can't believe it! I didn't even *think* about lying down I felt so good!"

That was the end of Marcie's misery — except for one time a couple of years later when she neglected to follow the therapy.

It was also the beginning of "Joyce Jones, Nutrition Consultant." From that time on, I started getting calls from friends — and friends of friends — asking if I knew of any nutritional remedy for this or that health problem. No doubt my college degree lent me some credibility, but it turned out that the most valuable advice I was able to offer them I'd learned as a direct result of my search for answers to help Darren.

CHAPTER 29

Epiphany

A new addition to the Jones household after we were settled in Manning was cable TV. I had not been in favor of it at first. Who needed all that violence and confusion and whatever else cable TV would bring into our home? However, Tom stood firm. It would make for better TV reception and there were some programs worth watching that could only be seen on cable. As for the undesirable ones, well, there *was* an off switch.

Much to my surprise, I soon discovered an interesting program — a Christian talk show — which I happened on one morning when I was working in the family room where the TV was enthroned.

After all our questions about our experiences in metaphysics, this program opened up a whole new vista. Through our involvement with metaphysics, both of us had acknowledged the existence of a spiritual world — something beyond that which could be perceived by the senses. It was usually benevolent, sometimes puzzling, occasionally frightening...and consistently out of reach. We had discovered that metaphysics promised great things, but only seemed to deliver to a select few.

On this show, I heard of a spiritual relationship with God that I had never thought possible, no matter the claims of the proponents of metaphysics. God was a real part of the lives of these people I saw on TV. He was Someone to whom they brought their deepest needs and found answers. Here was a relationship that went far beyond going to church on Sunday and trying to be a good person the rest of the week. I couldn't get enough of it. This was what I had been looking for all my life! I made a point of having something to do in the family room whenever the program was on.

One memorable morning Johanna Michaelson — the author of *The Beautiful Side of Evil* — gave an account of her experience with the occult. Here was a woman who had innocently become interested in astrology and fortune telling as a young girl and then had been drawn into psychic healing because of a deep desire to help others. Her experiences paralleled ours in many ways.

Johanna emphasized that the healings she had witnessed and taken part in were not hocus pocus. Miraculous things *had* actually happened, although many of her experiences were bizarre and sometimes frightening. People *were* actually healed. But she insisted the miracles did not come from God.

Not from God? I puzzled. Where then? Johanna's lengthy answer to that question was frightening. The essence of her response was that her involvement in psychic healing had culminated in a nightmare entanglement with demons!

A chill shot through me. We had vowed long ago that we would try anything that wouldn't hurt Darren. If what this woman was saying was true, our dabbling in metaphysics certainly didn't fall into the category of "wouldn't hurt." Instead it meant quite the opposite — that we had been dealing with the forces of Satan!

But Satan didn't perform good deeds for people, did he? Up to this point, I hadn't given reality of Satan's existence much thought. But the Bible said Satan existed, so it must be true. Johanna recounted the warnings in the Old Testament regarding prophets who worked miracles and would entice God's people to follow other gods and take up the practices of their pagan neighbors — divination, soothsaying, sorcery. The Bible called such practices abominations!

Had *we* been following the practices of "other gods"? I thought of Evelyn and her shadow guides...Doan Keegan, the mind reading, energy auras, dreams and visions...Clay Calder and the astrology readings...

It had sounded so good — the promise of wholeness, achieving one's full potential, self-esteem, helping others, creating a better world. And all this amid quotations from the Bible. But that very Bible forbade the things they were practicing! Suddenly it was as though a light had been turned on in my mind. Their "God" was not the God of the Bible; their "Jesus" was not the Son of God who had come to earth to die for the sins of humankind!

How could we have been so foolish!

Another chill shot through me when Johanna quoted from Deuteronomy 18:12: "All that do these things are an abomination unto the Lord."

Not only were these practices an abomination to God, but also *to those who do these things!* And while we hadn't actually *done* any of those things, we would have if we had been able to. We had wanted the power! We'd wanted it to control our own destinies – to control Darren's future.

Dabbling in the occult for power or any other reason is dangerous business. Why else would a loving God forbid it?

Johanna Michaelsen strongly warned parents about *Your Child and the Occult* in her book, *Like Lambs to the Slaughter*. She explains in detail how children and adults, even Christian believers, are easily drawn into the occult promises of self-empowerment, self-enlightenment and self-glorification. The opportunities *are* out there, even for children, as is evident in the popular Harry Potter books in which the young hero is going to a special school to learn sorcery. A school teaching Harry to "empower himself" with the assistance or the control of evil spirits...how to inflict spells and curses on others...how to use real world mechanics of witchcraft for his own gain. Just fantasy fiction? The American publisher, Scholastic Books, supplies our school systems with enormous amounts of Harry Potter books and promotes books that actually direct children to websites where they may find instructions on whatever form of sorcery, witchcraft or empowerment, they may wish to learn. We can only say, "BEWARE!"

Johanna herself was not delivered from demonic empowerment and authority until she surrendered herself to Jesus Christ as her Lord and Savior.

Tom and I had both claimed Jesus as our Savior when we were children in Sunday School, but God had never been a really important part in either of our lives. How shallow our claims had been! Now we felt an overwhelming need to surrender ourselves to Christ. To give Him the power and authority. To know Him. To *really* know Him!

Our ventures into metaphysics had made us realize as never before that there is more to the world than we can see or put our hands on. In our ignorance we had been taken in by the promises of the gurus...of being in charge of our own destiny, having the power ourselves to do good in the world, ushering in a wonderful new age of doing it our way, not God's way. But it was all in the wrong direction—away from Jesus Christ, the Son of God, the only one who can make everything turn out all right in the end...for Darren, for our whole family, for the world.

We had been treading on forbidden and dangerous ground. When we came to this realization, we no longer wanted any connection with metaphysics. We gathered together all the books, pamphlets, study guides, the health and astrology readings and everything else that we had accumulated in our pursuit of that deceptive, false rainbow and burned them. We made Jesus Christ, the Son of God, the Lord of our lives.

Now that we had removed all the material evidence of this harmful path we had mistakenly followed, there were still some hopes and promises connected with our exploration into metaphysics that we found difficult to discard. We had to let go of the dream that had been planted in our minds that by the time Darren was twenty, he would have outgrown his retardation—if he was retarded at all. What about the warning that he must avoid horses and motorcycles? What if he later became interested in horses or motorcycles? How should we react? This would come back to haunt us many times in the future, so we decided we would ask God to guide us! Trust in Him!

* * * * *

One evening as I carried a cup of tea upstairs to bed, I tripped and spilled the almost boiling liquid on my sock-covered foot. I quickly removed the sock from my throbbing foot, and a blister had already started to form across the top of it. I went to bed that night with my foot packed in ice.

Since I was unable to sleep because of the excruciating pain, I instead started to pray for relief. The thought suddenly occurred me that although this was the worst pain I had ever experienced, it was nothing compared to what Jesus suffered when he died on the cross for our sins. My pain disappeared instantly and I went to sleep praising and thanking God. In the morning there wasn't even a blister left—just a slight mark so I would know it had really happened. Some people have "burning bush" experiences like Moses in the Old Testament...for me it was a "burning foot!"

Our journey has been long and often hard, but this was proof to me that now we *were* going in the right direction. It was also clear to me that we make the most progress in realizing our God is real when we come upon detours and roadblocks! He is always with us and His

Holy Spirit lives within us. His ways are far above ours. Even rocky paths when given to God are made smooth.

We wondered why we held back from becoming even more involved in metaphysics. Why we didn't become entangled as so many others have? Then the old phrase "There but for the grace of God go I" came into my mind. Why He chose to intervene, we don't know, but we are overwhelmed with gratitude. Just like the man who despaired because he only saw one set of footprints on the sand when he was in a dire time of need, who was reassured by God that the footprints were His as he gently carried the man through his troubles—God had carried us away from the harmful path we had been following without us even being aware of His help!

Thank You! Thank You, Lord! To You *alone* be the glory!

CHAPTER 30

Educable or Trainable?

Suddenly it was September and time for school to start again. Andrea was enrolled in third grade at Metcalf, the elementary school on our side of town. And Darren was assigned to the Special Ed Trainable class.

"Trainable!" I exclaimed in disbelief when the secretary called from the principal's office. "There must be some mistake!"

"Trainable" was a term that was going out of vogue in Special Education by then, but it indicated a program that to my thinking amounted to little beyond baby sitting. No effort was made to teach reading because it was assumed that "trainable" children could not learn to read.

But Darren *was* learning to read so he definitely did not belong in the trainable class. His teacher in Stanton — Mrs. Moore — had advised me to make sure he was *never* placed in a trainable classroom…he *was* learning!

The secretary informed me that I would have to take my objections to the principal, Mr. Keller, who was not available until the next morning.

I worried for the rest of the day and hoped a call to the principal would take care of the matter as it had when

Darren had been so miserable in that kindergarten class at Cromwell Community Center.

When I finally reached Mr. Keller on the phone, I learned that the placement had been made by the school psychologist, who apparently had the final word on such matters.

"But my son is already learning to read," I objected. "It's all there in his records that we brought from Stanton. He doesn't belong in this trainable class."

"I"m sure Ms. Simms has her reasons for putting him in that class," Mr. Keller assured me.

"But she hasn't even met him!" I objected again.

He refused to listen to me so the telephone conversation ended up accomplishing nothing. It just left me with many confused questions. Did the method for placing Special Ed students have anything to do with class size? And if the trainable class was the smallest, was that where the next new Special Ed student was placed?

But none of that mattered to us because we were sure that it would be a mistake to enroll Darren in the trainable class. We couldn't bear to think of his being shuffled off into the trainable class with nothing to stimulate him. Not after the progress he had made last year. And the Manning superintendent of schools *had* said that "the law" mandated suitable placement of a student. We decided that even temporary placement would not be good. Moving and changing schools was enough of a change without Darren also being placed in this trainable class that was the equivalent of keeping him back a year. We wanted him to continue to read and learn and make progress!

* * * * *

So trying not to make a big a deal out of it, I explained to the kids that Darren wouldn't be going to school until we straightened out which class he would be in. Darren didn't care and Andrea didn't understand, but she went off to school glad that *she* wasn't the one who had to stay home.

As soon as she left, I called the principal and requested that Darren's placement be reconsidered, again referring to his records and the recommendations of his last teacher. "I would be glad to have a conference with Ms. Simms," I said, "and if she wants to test him, that's fine. I'll be keeping him home until this is straightened out. We don't want him upset and confused by having to change classes."

"I understand how you feel, Mrs. Jones," Mr. Keller said, "but I think you are making a mistake in keeping your son out of school and I hope you will reconsider. However, I will discuss the matter with Ms. Simms, though I can't promise you anything."

Mr. Keller called back on Wednesday to inform me that if I still felt that Darren should be in the other class, they would place him there on a trial basis.

It was an incomplete victory — and we soon wondered if it was a victory at all.

I took Darren to school the first morning to observe the class as I always did. He arrived in high spirits, anticipating the new friends he would make and the fun things that would be going on at school. But he left feeling completely different.

"No more school!" he declared at the end of the day. He declared that it wasn't fun at all, he didn't like the kids and he didn't like the teacher. And he never changed his mind.

Every morning I would pry him out of bed and then use every trick I could think of to get him dressed, fed and off to school.

Not only was Darren unhappy with school, school was unhappy with Darren. Toward the end of the second week his teacher, Mrs. Harman, called to inform me that he was being uncooperative and disruptive in class. I went in for a conference before school the next morning. Not much was accomplished except to reestablish the already-known fact that there was a problem. Finally, after several more days of complaints on both sides, I asked if I could come in again to observe the class. Mrs. Harmon was not particularly enthusiastic about the idea but grudgingly gave her permission for a short visit—with the emphasis on "short."

I didn't go there with the idea that I would come up with some brilliant way to take care of Darren's problems. I knew they weren't usually so easily disposed of. However, one problem was almost immediately evident. It was a learning disability class – far too high functioning for Darren. The constant coming and going of the students, I presume, had to do with mainstreaming the students into the regular classrooms, but it certainly didn't make for a conducive learning atmosphere for Darren. It wasn't quite as wild and disruptive as Cromwell kindergarten had been…but almost.

I also noticed that Darren was the *only* one *not* involved in the coming and going. He sat fidgeting at his desk with a worksheet in front of him. Occasionally he absently scribbled on the sheet, but he was obviously distracted by all the activity going on around him. Several times he got up and started to wander around the room— probably trying to join in all the activity. Each time, Mrs. Harman or her aid sent him back to his seat with firm orders to get to work, which produced absolutely nothing but more fidgeting and scribbling.

I thought some help from the teacher to get him started might be in order. After all, wasn't that what Special Ed was all about—*specialized* education? But what did a mere parent know? And what could I do?

One ray of hope was Darren's IEP—the Individual Education Program that was part of a 1975 law (P.L. 94-

142) that the Manning superintendent of schools had told us would ensure that our handicapped child would be provided the same educational opportunities as any other child in the least restricted environment. So a meeting was scheduled for the following week with Darren's teachers and others involved in his education. We'd be there! We were going to make sure our son got the education he was legally entitled to receive.

CHAPTER 31

Showing His Colors

Tom took time off from work to attend the meeting about Darren's IEP. But we were disappointed to find out that it was all pretty much cut and dried. So much so that after it was all over, we knew the only reason we had been invited was because the law dictated that parents be included in the planning of their child's education. We were merely observers and too ignorant and inexperienced in the workings of Special Ed to object.

It was all over in about a half hour. Although we were never told directly, one thing we did learn from listening in was that Darren's placement in this class was no longer in question. Mrs. Harman had conceded that in spite of his many problems, he *could* be educated.

The magic word "mainstreaming" was bandied about quite a bit during that conference. For Darren, this meant that the regular first grade would be his "homeroom." He would report there every morning, go to recess and lunch with the first graders and join them for their gym, art and music classes once a week. The rest of his time at school would be spent in the Special Ed room in the "Learning Disabled" class. We wondered just what he would do there, but didn't venture to ask. Instead we meekly signed the paper outlining Darren's program for the year and went home, hoping the professionals knew what they were doing. We were also hoping that the mainstreaming would help to make school more tolerable for Darren.

Unfortunately that didn't happen. The daily battle to get him off to school continued. I decided another visit to school was in order, even though my last one had been depressingly unproductive.

I spent the entire morning at school, following Darren from his first grade homeroom to the Special Ed classroom and back again to a first grade activity. I was still troubled by the continual coming and going of the Special Ed students because I noticed that each departure and arrival commanded Darren's full attention whether or not it involved him. Now, with the mainstreaming, I was disappointed that he remained forlornly on the fringes of whatever the activity in the first grade classroom.

When he worked at the chalkboard under the direction of Mrs. Harman, I noticed he had a great deal of trouble copying the numbers written at the *top* of the board. His difficulties made me wonder if his sight was an even bigger problem than we had thought. Was it possible that he couldn't see the numbers Mrs. Harman wanted him to copy? Or did he just not understand what she wanted? Or was he simply being difficult?

We had his eyes examined yearly to make sure that the toxoplasmosis that damaged his eyes before birth remained in a dormant state, as well as taking him for periodic checkups since he began wearing glasses when he was two. Although the prescription had been changed a couple of times, we had not yet been convinced that the glasses actually helped...but who were we to say? Now we began to wonder if more extensive testing was available. Maybe we ought to find out.

I called Mrs. Harman to discuss our concerns regarding Darren's sight problems. She gave us the impression that she felt his difficulties were more contrariness than anything else, but nevertheless suggested contacting Mr. Graham, the Special Ed Director. After I talked with him, he did some checking around, and when he called me back he suggested that we contact the state School for the Blind.

"School for the Blind?" I asked in confusion. "But he can *see!*" My recent dealings with Special Ed people were making me defensive and suspicious, so I was worried that this man was giving me the run around too.

He explained that the institution also worked with people with severe sight handicaps and told me about one student he knew who had shown great improvement after being referred there. As he continued, I decided that maybe Mr. Graham was more knowledgeable and caring than I had first thought.

I wrote down the number he gave me and called the School for the Blind. The information Mr. Graham had given me proved to be correct, but they suggested that we should first contact Dr. Schmidt, an ophthalmologist who would give Darren a thorough examination—and then we could proceed from there. Although he was not connected to the school, he apparently worked closely with them and came highly recommended. Unfortunately, the doctor didn't have an opening until after Christmas. Not having any other direction to go at the moment, I took the earliest appointment they had. We'd tough it out until after Christmas.

* * * * *

Meanwhile life went on and so did school. Andrea came home one day and quietly announced that a mean third grade boy who had been teasing Darren on the playground wouldn't be doing it anymore.

How did she know that? Well, today while she was playing tether ball with some of her friends, she saw this boy picking on Darren, so she ran right up to him, grabbed the front of his shirt and slammed him against the brick wall of the school building and said, "If I ever see you teasing my brother again, I'll beat you to a pulp!"

We found it a little difficult to visualize our sweet little Andrea being able to stop a bully. Maybe it was the shock element? In any case, she was right. He stopped picking on Darren! As time went on, we learned through various sources that Andrea had a reputation of looking out for the underdog — whether it was her brother or someone else.

* * * * *

The week before Thanksgiving, Darren brought home a large manila sheet with black scribbles over some brighter colors which he declared was a turkey.

"I said 'lots of colors.' I want *black*," he said grimly when I asked about his picture. Apparently he and the art teacher had had a conflict — whether or not she was aware of it. So now that he was home, he got a black crayon and colored over all the other colors until there was nothing but black. It was almost a violent action. Then instead of putting the drawing on the front of the refrigerator where we kept an ongoing display of his and Andrea's artwork, he wadded it up and threw it into the wastebasket. He looked up at me defiantly, as though daring me to challenge his action. There was obviously more to this than just his choice of colors. It seemed to be a rebellious expression of Darren's whole unhappy experience in school this year.

"You don't want to keep it?" I asked, hoping to draw him out.

"I hate it!" he said and stomped out of the room. I was sure "it" included much more than the drawing.

Darren caught a cold during Thanksgiving and by the time I felt that he was well enough to go out into the world again — both for his own good and that of the general public — he had missed almost two weeks of school. It was actually a relief to have a valid reason to keep him home since I got a respite from the daily battle of getting him up and off to school. Unfortunately, it wasn't long enough for him to forget how much he hated school, so it was even harder to convince him to go back. But Christmas was coming! Surely, that would help to brighten up his mood?

CHAPTER 32

Christmas Ups and Downs

For us Christmas meant finding a real tree chosen in the woods where it was growing. Since the holiday was fast approaching, we all piled into the station wagon one Saturday morning and drove out to the tree farm. It took some tramping around, but we finally found one that everyone agreed on—tall enough to almost touch the vaulted living room ceiling, full and about as perfectly shaped as an evergreen could get.

When it was cut down, Tom hoisted it to the top of the station wagon and was beginning to tie it on when he saw something move on one of the branches near the top of the tree! Then two tiny bright eyes peered out at him for half a second and disappeared.

"Well, looks like we've got some livestock with our tree—there's a mouse in there!" he announced.

"Oh, let me see! Let me see!" Darren shouted, jumping up and down, trying to climb up on the car for a better view.

"Shoo! Shoo!" Tom said, shaking the branches where he had seen the mouse.

"I don't think he came out, Dad," Andrea said, running around the car in hopes of seeing the mouse make its escape.

Tom shook the tree quite vigorously while Darren watched up close and Andrea and I stood back at some distance. No mouse…

"Oh well," Tom said, "it'll blow off when we get going down the road. It'll be gone by the time we get home."

Andrea and Darren watched all the way home, hoping to see the mouse make its flying departure.

But when we got there and Tom started to untie the tree and take it off the car roof, there were those two tiny, bright eyes peering at him from a branch farther down. Tom slid the tree onto the ground and again shook the tree energetically. The mouse still didn't abandon its shelter.

"Somebody get Muffin," Tom said, still shaking the tree, "Westies are supposed to be good mousers." Muffin was in the house barking excitedly and bounded out happily when Darren opened the door. She had never had any experience with mice as far as we knew, but she was definitely interested in what was going on.

"Now, let's get organized," Tom said, having given up on shaking the tree. "Everyone get a stick or a broom and start poking and beating at the tree from one end to chase the mouse to the other."

While Muffin barked, we all found our weapons and started poking and beating. The neighbors were peeking out from behind their curtains watching, probably wondering what sort of strange Christmas ritual the Jones family was performing.

It seemed like we poked at the tree forever until at last the mouse appeared and went skittering off across the yard and around the corner of the house with Muffin close behind.

No one knows what happened after that but Muffin… and she never told. The only clue was that throughout that Christmas season and every year after that, Muffin was the Keeper of the Tree. Whether she was hoping for another mouse for her own entertainment or protecting her family, as soon as a tree was brought into the house, Muffin was always there — watching...

When the tree was anchored in its holder, it came close to touching the ceiling as we had hoped, and was just what we had in mind. We all agreed it was the nicest tree we ever had.

"Almost seems a shame to put decorations on it," Tom said. "It's beautiful just like it is."

"But we gotta have lights and angels and stuff!" Darren objected.

"Oh, sure, we will. Don't worry," Tom reassured him.

"And Mom, don't forget the decorations you found at that rummage sale," Andrea reminded me.

Last spring at a big church rummage sale in Stanton, I had discovered a dented shoe box tied with string and labeled in black crayon "For Jesse Tree." When I opened the box, I discovered a collection of what appeared to be Christmas tree ornaments packed in crumpled tissue paper. They were all made of wood and looked hand carved and painted. They were obviously old — the paint on some was worn — and absolutely lovely! Naturally, I bought them.

I wondered when I had taken them all out of the box if they actually were Christmas tree decorations. Although there was a star and a camel, most of the other shapes — including a houseboat, a ladder, a fish and a wheel — didn't seem to have anything to do with Christmas. No doubt the solution to the mystery lay in finding out what a Jesse Tree was. I asked a number of people but no one knew. No matter. They would make lovely Christmas tree decorations.

Andrea came bounding in from school one afternoon and announced that she had learned what a Jesse Tree was from a book about Christmas customs in the library. "It's a tree decorated with ornaments that remind us of people all through the Bible who helped get the world ready for Jesus to come," she said. "It's called a Jesse Tree because that was the name of the father of David in the Bible — you know the shepherd boy who became a king — and Jesus came from his family."

"Well, that's interesting," I said. "Sort of a family tree, maybe? Did the book say which people the different ornaments stood for?"

"No, all it said was what I told you. But we could have fun figuring that out."

And so we did, though it took a little time. It turned out to be a thought provoking study of just who Jesus is and why he came. Some of the symbols were easy. The little golden harp was for David, of course. The houseboat was probably Noah's ark. But what did that have to do with Jesus' coming? And the lion must represent Daniel, but how was Daniel connected with the coming of Jesus? Darren came up with the best answer for the red heart. "It's for God," he insisted. "Because a heart means love. And God loves us and that's why Jesus came!"

Good thinking, Darren!

Visitors during the holidays were always fascinated with our unique ornaments and with the help of friends knowledgeable in Biblical prophecy, over time we cleared up the mystery of the connection of Noah's ark, Daniel and even Ezekiel's wheel with the coming of Jesus, the Messiah.

* * * * *

Both Andrea and Darren had brought home announcements about the school Christmas musical program. Andrea's was neatly decorated with red and green crayon and Darren's was scribbled all over in black. Everything Darren brought home these days was scribbled over in black. Andrea had been talking about the part the third grade would contribute to the program for some time now. Darren would be performing with the first grade but he didn't talk about it, except to declare several times in no uncertain terms that he was *not* going to be in the program.

The day of the program he came home from school looking like a thundercloud, which I attributed to his unhappiness about the upcoming program, although I didn't ask. He would let us know sooner or later.

The storm descended at the dinner table when I suggested that he stop playing with his food and finish eating so he could get ready for the program. He jumped up from the table, raced into the living room and flung himself on the sofa. "Not going! Not going! Not going!" he yelled. He thumped his heels on the floor to add emphasis to his words.

Tom and I looked at one another, each hoping the other had some magic up his sleeve that would persuade Darren to be cooperative. We had already talked it over and felt that it would be good for him to take part in the program.

We no longer remember how it happened, but through some miracle Darren did relent and we all went to the program.

But that evening after the kids had gone to bed we mulled over the evening and decided that we had been mistaken to think it was in Darren's best interests to participate in the Christmas program. We were still smarting over a remark someone behind us had made while the first graders were performing.

"What's the matter with that stupid, funny-looking kid wearing the blue sweater in the front row? Somebody ought to straighten him up!" a voice behind us had whispered maliciously.

That "stupid, funny-looking kid wearing the blue sweater in the front row" just happened to be our Darren. And we had to admit that it looked as though he needed some straightening up. Being one of the smaller ones in the group, he was conspicuous in the front row — wriggling, fidgeting and looking around — completely disconnected from the rest of the group. Everyone else was singing enthusiastically, their attention focused on Mrs. Jennings, the music teacher.

"I wonder if he could even *see* Mrs. Jennings," I mused. "And if he couldn't, how could he possibly know what he was supposed to do? She could have been giving him all kinds of signals, but he had no way of knowing it."

Tom sighed deeply. "What *is* the answer for Darren? Mainstreaming sounded great on paper, but I think it's making him hate school all the more. He doesn't fit in and he knows it!"

"I do wonder sometimes if there are any answers for this school situation," I said, close to tears. "But I keep telling myself, 'There's got to be! Look how far he's come...this little kid that was supposed to be a vegetable'."

We didn't want to believe that the progress would stop. Surely there was a purpose behind it all and it was going to turn out all right in the end — good would overcome if we just hung in there.

I was praying with Darren and Andrea on Christmas night before tucking them in for the night when I was interrupted.

"Mom," Darren said, patting my arm insistently, "I want to talk about Christmas presents — what I got for Christmas."

"Just a minute, Darren. After we finish praying." I thought a discussion about Christmas presents could wait for just a minute.

Apparently it couldn't. "I *really* want to talk about Christmas presents," Darren interrupted again a moment later.

I gave up. "All right, what is it?"

"Well, I got lots of nice things," he began hesitantly, "but I didn't need "em. All I really need is *love*."

"And you got both gifts and love?" I asked, hoping that was what he meant.

"Yeah!" he replied contentedly.

I hugged him tight, unable to say anything.

CHAPTER 33

What's Life All About?

Tom took Darren for his appointment with the ophthalmologist, Dr. Schmidt. It's being a three hour drive one way, they left before daylight and didn't get home until that evening.

Darren trailed sleepily into the house behind Tom, not wearing his glasses.

"What happened to his glasses?" I asked in concern.

"Don't do any good," Darren informed me matter of factly.

I looked questioningly at Tom who just shrugged. "That's what Dr. Schmidt said — and that they probably didn't do any harm — but why should he wear them if they don't help?" Then in an aside so Darren couldn't hear he added, "Worse problems than we realized. I'll tell you later."

Darren gave me a run down of the day as I tucked him into bed. He told me the doctor had lots of things to look at and that was "kinda fun — like watching TV, sorta." But the best part was that it was "just me and Dad." And you and Andrea stayed home."

Well, thanks a lot, Darren! But I was truly glad they'd had a good time together.

After the kids were settled in bed, Tom told me the examination had revealed essentially the same condition the doctors at University Hospital had diagnosed when Darren was just a baby — scar tissue present since birth. Now we had learned the effect of that scar tissue.

"He's legally blind!" Tom said bluntly, not able to keep the anguish out of his voice.

I was enveloped by a flush of emotion and my heart leapt into my throat so that I couldn't even cry out my objections.

"Twenty over two hundred," Tom continued gloomily. "Objects twenty feet away appear to Darren as they would to a person with normal vision at a distance of two hundred feet. That's legally blind. Sometimes it's as high as twenty over seven hundred. And there are holes in his vision. What he sees is like looking at a puzzle with several pieces missing, only not always the same pieces. His central vision is non-existent. He only sees peripherally. I wonder how he can make any sense out of what he sees."

I sat numbly trying to digest what Tom had just told me. "It would be like seeing…well, like seeing confusing chaos!" I said finally.

"I guess that would be an accurate way to describe it."

"And nothing can be done, I suppose."

"Not really. Just things to help him use what little sight he has to his best advantage."

"Like what?"

"Oh, having reading material with large print that's bold and black. There's a device that might help. Actually, it's an electronic magnifier…some call it a closed circuit TV. It enlarges print and makes it easier to see. The doctor doesn't usually recommend it because it's cumbersome to use and very expensive, but he thought it might be worth the trouble and expense in Darren's case. I think we ought to look into it."

When we checked it out, we made the happy discovery that we could actually borrow a closed circuit TV to try out.

Not surprisingly, there was a waiting list for the unit, but Darren's turn would come in a month or so.

In the meantime, armed with Dr. Schmidt's report and recommendations, I had another conference at school with Mrs. Harman—who was not enthusiastic about the recommendations. I resolved not to be intimidated. It was my mission to see that Darren got the education he needed, not make Mrs. Harman happy.

Just how it happened I don't know, but when the conference was over, it turned out that the special things Dr. Schmidt had recommended to help Darren in his school work became *my* responsibility, not the school's.

"That's fine if you want to try the closed circuit TV," Mrs. Harman said disinterestedly, "but we don't have the time or space for it here. And with Darren's short attention span, I doubt that it would help much anyway."

I was dismissed after a half hour or so with a packet of mimeographed worksheets that I was to trace over with a black marking pen since I didn't think they were black enough for Darren to see.

I hated to admit it, but in spite of my resolve, it looked like I'd been had. But what could I do? I traced over the worksheets and copied and enlarged all his reading stories with a black pen and sent them back to Mrs. Harman.

Darren's work did start showing some improvement with the new worksheets that were supposedly easier to see, so Mrs. Harman began sending sheets home for him to finish. In theory, I felt that this was probably a sound idea. It certainly was important for Darren to learn to finish a job. But in practice it also shifted the responsibility to good old Mom! After school time turned into a battle of wits to keep Darren on task to finish his schoolwork before bedtime. Sometimes I won. More often I didn't. In addition to poor vision, somewhere along the way, our Darren had become a master at dawdling. Getting him to do his work was like pushing a rope.

The closed circuit TV amazingly arrived much sooner than we had expected. I excitedly unpacked it and was reading the instruction booklet when Darren arrived home from school. Darren was actually eager to try it out although it was associated with schoolwork—probably because it resembled a TV!

"I can do it!" he insisted, pulling a chair up close.

I helped him put a worksheet in place according to the booklet's instructions that he'd brought home that day and let him twist the knob that turned it on.

"Hey, neat!" he exclaimed as the screen lit up, enlarging the words on the worksheet bright and black and clear. It also had a reverse switch that changed the background to black and the letters to white. That was even better...more contrast. He didn't have to use his nose to read that print! It took some practice to work on the sheet while it was in the machine, but I could see that it had great potential to really help him with his worksheet and the stories in his reading book. Dinner was a little late that evening, but by the time we ate Darren had read quite successfully through his assigned story for tomorrow and had already finished both worksheets Mrs. Harman had sent home!

And just for fun Darren had looked at coins with the new machine. "Look, there are pictures on them!" he exclaimed with excitement. "I thought they were just bumpy."

* * * * *

Naturally, we realized that the novelty of doing schoolwork on TV would wear off sooner or later. Nevertheless, it was obvious that the closed circuit TV made it less stressful for Darren to do his work as well as more interesting. If only there could be one at school!

There *should* be one at school! The more we thought about it, the more convinced we became. There might be other children besides Darren who would benefit. If there weren't any other children with severe visual problems now, surely there would be sooner or later. But how to convince the powers that be of this?

Not knowing where else to turn I decided to take our case to the Superintendent of Schools. He listened sympathetically while I presented my case for the closed circuit TV. I didn't bother to mention Mrs. Harman's lack of interest. We'd worry about that after we got the machine.

Yes, he could see that such an aid would be a real boon for visually handicapped children and there was at least one other child in the district with a severe visual handicap, though she was not yet in school. As usual the problem was money—and priority—but he would see what could be done.

At home, we poured over our own finances trying to figure out how we could pay for a closed circuit TV for Darren to use at home. We concluded that somehow we would manage. We'd do without something else...this was a priority item!

Needless to say, getting a closed circuit TV for Darren didn't solve all of his school problems since they weren't all visual, but it turned out to be well worth the sacrifice. A unit at school would have been even better, but that wasn't likely to come to pass any time soon.

* * * * *

One evening I was rummaging through a box we hadn't opened since our move and Andrea came across the Ungame©, a game we had enjoyed as a family in the past. I brought it downstairs and that evening after dinner I asked, "Anyone want to play?"

Without waiting for an answer, I peeled the rubber band off the pack of cards. "I'll just read a question and anyone can answer that wants to," I said, making up my own rules which we often did with this game. I read several cards, all of which evoked quick, if not intelligent, answers from the entire family.

Then I came to one that I thought might be a hard one, but I read the question anyway, "What is life all about?" Even Mom and Dad were struggling to answer— pondering deep intellectual and philosophical thoughts and doing some real soul-searching.

"That's easy…it's *love!*" Darren said matter-of-factly and almost instantly, as though everyone ought to know that.

We looked at each other dumbfounded. What a profound answer! Maybe we needed to give this boy more opportunities to express himself!

* * * * *

Not long after that Darren's mainstream teacher, Miss Barton, called to let us know that he had been involved in several fights the past few days. She hadn't been able to determine just what had set him off.

When Darren came home that day, I questioned him about Miss Barton's call. "You know it really makes me feel sad you are causing trouble like that," I added.

"Mom, you have to teach me how not to fight with kids before you die," he said earnestly. I suspected he was trying to distract me from possible discipline.

"Well, I"m not expecting to die any time soon," I told him, struggling not to smile, "but I think we'd better do something about this fighting at school. What's the problem? Why are you fighting?"

He climbed up on the kitchen stool, his shoulders hunched, his head hanging. "Dunno," he mumbled.

"Whatever happened to *love?*" I asked. I felt as though I was punching below the belt, but I did wonder considering his surprising response during the Ungame.

"Dunno," he mumbled again, his head hanging even lower.

I could see that this conversation was going nowhere with the "dunnos." Maybe he really didn't know why he was fighting and it was just part of the whole "I hate school" syndrome.

Trying a new tack, I asked, "You know what I don't know?"

"What?" he asked as he straightened up a little.

"How to teach you not to fight. Do you have any suggestions?"

"Well, you could say, 'Don't get mad at people and don't hit 'em and kick 'em and stuff like that.'" He sat up even straighter and continued, warming to his subject, "and you could say, 'do something nice to somebody even if they're not nice to you'."

"Darren! Those are very good suggestions! You already know how not to fight. I don't need to teach you!"

"Yeah, but I don't do 'em at school!" he said darkly.

A voice interrupted from the doorway. "You'd better start! Do you hear me?"

Dad had arrived home from work.

All the spunk surprised out of him, Darren nodded meekly and wriggled off his perch.

We didn't hear any more from Miss Barton about fighting after that. We had a little trouble picturing Darren putting into practice the doing "something nice to somebody even if they're not nice to you" part of his advice, but apparently he had at least given up the hitting and kicking and "stuff like that."

CHAPTER 34

Walking on Water

When summer finally arrived that year—signaling the end of the school year— it had never been more welcome as far as I was concerned! No more battles with Darren to get him off to school every morning. No more sparring for Darren's educational rights. I was worn out from it all.

One of the bright spots of early summer was swimming lessons. Both Andrea and Darren went happily shivering off to the city pool with sweat suits over their bathing suits those cool mornings in early June. They both loved swimming and Andrea was gathering quite a collection of certificates and awards for her achievements. Darren's progress wasn't quite as showy, but he had come a long way since that first lesson at the pool in Stanton when he was four—although he was still a skinny little kid in baggy trunks. Swimming was one of the few activities that he was able to participate in with some success, but unfortunately swimming lessons didn't last all summer.

"I got no one to play with!" Darren wailed one hot summer afternoon as he watched Andrea ride off on her bike with a couple of girls she had become acquainted with at school.

I thought with longing of those golden summer days back in Stanton when the neighborhood kids were in and out of the house and yard all day long. It had been hectic, but a good kind of hectic.

"You know, what I need is a brother!" Darren declared suddenly, interrupting my reverie.

"Now that's an idea!" I said. "The problem is that it would take a baby brother a long time to get big enough to play with."

"No, not a *baby* brother! One about three years old!"

"But you don't just get a three year old brother. He would have to be a baby first and then grow up to be three."

"Yeah, I know that. But I want a three year old brother, not a baby brother!"

"Why three years old?" I couldn't resist asking.

""Cause that would be big enough to do stuff. He could play with my toys and I could teach him things."

"You've got Muffin. Why don't you play with her?"

"Aw, Mom! Muffin's just a dog. I need a *brother!*"

"Well, maybe. But I'm afraid you'll have to be satisfied with a dog for now."

Darren brought up the subject again at bedtime prayers. "I really need a brother!" he said. "I"m going to ask God about getting me a brother."

"All right," I said, "but remember that we don't always get what we pray for. God knows better than we do what we ought to have."

"Yeah, but I really *do* need a brother," Darren insisted. That night he began talking in earnest to God about getting a three year old brother.

A couple of days later, I was away for the evening so Tom supervised the bedtime rituals.

"Hey, what's this about Darren getting a little brother?" Tom asked when I came home.

"*His* idea, not mine!"

"Maybe we ought to think about it."

"You are kidding, aren't you? It's a *three year old* brother he wants you know."

"Maybe we could find an orphan around somewhere that no one wants."

"You and your orphans!" I teased.

* * * * *

One of the drawbacks to Tom's new job was that he was required to work Saturday mornings. And so it was that one Saturday morning late in the summer—one of those balmy days perfect for sailing—Tom took me, the kids and the sailboat out to the lake just outside of town on his way to work. He would join us later when he had finished his morning work.

The small lake was surrounded by hills and sometimes sudden gusts of wind swept across the lake. I was just getting everyone settled on the boat—making sure that Darren was firmly holding the rails on each side of the boat, then getting the rudder set just right with one hand while the other held the line to the sail—when one of those gusty winds took me by surprise.

If you are in trouble, one of the first rules of sailing is to let go of the line to the sail. This lets the sail point directly into the wind and returns the boat to a stable position. Unfortunately, I was so occupied with the business of getting settled that sailing rules were far from my mind. Holding the line to the sail to keep from sliding off the boat was the natural inclination, but the wrong thing to do on a sailboat. The sail suddenly filled with wind—too much wind—and I slipped off the capsizing boat and into the water. I had made sure the kids had on life jackets, but I, being a good swimmer, wasn't wearing one and I found myself plunging down, down into the water. It seemed like an eternity before I surfaced. When I did, the sail was lying on top of the water and the boat was perpendicular to the water with the mast still attached. Andrea was bobbing on the water, safe and sound in her life jacket...but where was Darren? In a panic, I scanned the area calling his name. Was he caught under the sail? No. Then Andrea shouted, "Look Mom! There he is—*walking on the water!*"

Sure enough! There he was—holding on to the rail on one side of the boat with both hands and standing on the rail on the other side—so it looked like he actually was walking on water! We all began laughing hysterically—both in sheer relief and at the sight of Darren walking on the water—while I righted the boat so we could scramble back on.

This time I was careful to point the boat more into the wind and finally we were really sailing, Andrea and I enjoying the scenery while the breeze whipped through our wet hair.

Not able to see the scenery, Darren was ready for some more adventure. "Mom," he said, "tipping the boat over was fun. Let's do it again!"

CHAPTER 35

A Light at the End
of the Tunnel

September arrived and with it came the same old battle to get Darren off to school every morning. Nothing about school had changed since last year as far as he was concerned. How were we going to survive another school year? I prayed for daily patience, strength and wisdom. On some of the more grim days I could only cry out in desperation, "Help, Lord!"

Then we learned about the Christian Academy in the nearby town of Johnstown. Several families from Manning sent their children there, and everyone who knew anything about it described it as a good school although it was "religious"...whatever *that* meant.

When I called for information, Mr. Randall,who was the principal, explained to me that although they didn't have a program specifically for handicapped children, that didn't mean they wouldn't consider taking a handicapped child. So he invited me to come by and discuss our situation with him.

During our meeting I did my best to give a complete and honest picture of Darren and his problems. After all, if they enrolled him they would find out soon enough. Mr. Randall then outlined the philosophy of the school, which put a great deal of emphasis on teaching both Christian and academic basics. At the end of the interview, I was quite favorably impressed with Johnstown Christian Academy.

The bottom line was would – or *could* – the academy accept Darren as a student? There would have to be a meeting of the staff to see what could be worked out.

Mr. Randall called two days later to let us know they had decided that we could enroll our son in the academy on a one month trial basis in their kindergarten classroom, which he informed us was more like first grade in public school.

We had already decided that Darren would do better in a kindergarten class than the Special Ed class he'd been attending in public school until now. We had actually become so eager to effect *some* change in Darren's education during the last school year, that we had taken him to The Meyer Children's Rehabilitation Institute in another state – at our own expense – because we so desperately wanted an expert opinion as to his proper placement. (We later found out that the school system should have paid for that trip.) The Institute had agreed with us and sent us home with a written recommendation for Darren's schooling, but no action had been taken to comply with it because the Manning Superintendent did not even have to acknowledge out of state recommendations. So for whatever reason...he never did.

Now of course we would have preferred to see Darren happily mainstreamed into a loving class of third graders. After all, he was eight years old. But deep down we knew that wasn't being realistic. The academic skills – and social, too, for that matter – that he needed to work on were definitely at the kindergarten/first grade level. And being small for his age he wouldn't be conspicuously out of place. Although the idea of the trial period was cause for some hesitation, if the private school didn't work out as we hoped, we would have to eat humble pie and put him back in Mrs. Harman's class—and it was difficult facing that possibility. Taking Darren out of public school was a big step.

Knowing full well that momentous decisions such as this should be slept on at least one night, we spent a couple of days thinking it over. Somewhere in our budget we would have to find the not-so-negligible sum it would cost to send a child to private school. Plus it would probably be two children when all was said and done because we felt that it would be best for all concerned if both children attended the same school. Could we swing it? We found that with some belt tightening, mainly in the category of automobiles, we could. Tom would make do with the aging second car he drove to work, instead of replacing it with a newer one as we had planned. If it gave out, we'd just have to manage without a second car.

Before we made our final decision I went back to Johnstown to meet Mrs. Lawson, who would be Darren's new teacher, and visited her kindergarten classroom.

That clinched it. I believe Marsha Lawson is the kind of teacher *every* child should have at least once in their life. She was a sturdy, rosy-cheeked young woman with an aura about her that engendered a feeling of order and peace within the classroom while still inspiring her students to participate with enthusiasm. After only a short time in the classroom, I could sense that these students were studying and learning for the sheer joy of it. I longed for Darren to have that experience. Dare I hope?

As for Darren himself, we had casually mentioned the possibility of his going to another school, both to get his reaction to the idea and to prepare him in case it should come to pass. He would have been the *most* receptive to forgetting the idea of school altogether and staying at home doing what he pleased. The thought of not having to go back to the old school—even if that meant going to *another* school—had a very strong appeal.

I was even more convinced that we were doing the right thing for Darren when Mrs. Harman received the news that we were transferring him to a private school with ill-concealed joy—although she did have the good grace to wish him well.

* * * * *

The following Monday morning Andrea eagerly marched into the fifth/sixth grade room at Johnstown Christian Academy while I delivered Darren—feet slightly dragging—to his new kindergarten class.

Several children came bounding over happily to greet us.

"Mrs. Lawson, here's that new boy, Darren!" a little boy announced in an "isn't this perfectly wonderful!" voice.

Darren wasn't used to anyone being that glad to see him. Suddenly his feet weren't dragging at all. With scarcely a backward glance in my direction, he allowed himself to be swept into the room to get acquainted with the other children. I stood at the door for a few moments watching the magic of Mrs. Lawson's classroom unfold.

On the way home I reflected with misty eyes that when I wrote my *Handbook for Teachers on Mainstreaming Handicapped Children*—while realizing I had never thought about writing any handbook until that very moment!—there should be a chapter entitled"Preparing the Class." It appeared that Mrs. Lawson would be a very credible expert in that field!

Darren still acted like Darren at the academy, but the black moods disappeared and he quite happily boarded the academy van every morning when it stopped in front of our house.

In fact as far as the van ride was concerned, he soon got a little *too* happy. The second week he came home with a note. "Dear Mrs. Jones," it read, "We regret to inform you that Darren's behavior is unacceptable according to the rules of the van. Please try to calm him down! We have tried to calm him down but failed. From, everyone on the van."

After briefly questioning Andrea, I was able to piece together what had been happening. I was quite relieved when I understood the problem was *not* that *all* of the other children on the van were exceptionally well behaved as the goody-goody tone of the note sounded. Darren was just trying to fit in by imitating their behavior…except he got too carried away and ended up being twice as loud and silly as everyone else. But it was still time for a little talk!

"Darren, you know that on the van you are to sit quietly in your seat…" I began my lecture.

"Yeah," Darren agreed, adding sagely, "If someone else doesn't know how to behave, that's *their* problem and the van driver's. I don't want to act like them!"

Exactly! I hoped his actions would match his words.

Day by day dear Mrs. Lawson continued to live up to my first impression of her, even throwing in a few nice surprises now and then. The most stupendous of these surprises was the whole hearted acceptance by Mrs. Lawson of a closed circuit TV that I had been able to acquire for Darren to use at school. With a few simple phone calls to a government agency, I was able to have a unit placed in Darren's classroom in this little private school with no government connections. This was something the public school and teachers were not willing or able to do. But one day, there it was! And what a difference it made in Darren's schoolwork to have that visual help at school as well as at home. Although Darren's reading was still slow, with the help of the electronic magnifier his reading speed increased eightfold. At long last, he was beginning to make some progress again in school.

Utopia lasted until the end of that first school year. Tragedy of tragedies — as far as we were concerned! — Mrs. Lawson's husband took a new job out of state and she moved with him! Her replacement was a young woman fresh out of college named Miss Collins who, considering her inexperience, was competent enough. But she wasn't Mrs. Lawson.

About the same time that Miss Collins came on the scene, Darren began recounting stories about one of his classmates, Zachary.

Zachary, it seems, had to sit in the time-out chair three times in one day! Zachary had to stay in for recess! Zachary had to go to Mr. Randall's office for a long, long time! We weren't overly concerned about Zachary's escapades until Miss Collins called to inform me that Darren was beginning to follow in Zachary's footsteps. Who would have thought that our son would encounter a bad influence in a Christian school?

The next time it was my turn to drive the van, I stopped to visit Miss Collin's class. Since it was a rainy day, Darren's gym class was inside. Miss Collins was supervising a game that involved an enormous white silk parachute, and she was looking agitated as I peeked in the door before entering unobserved. A child resembling an animated white silk lump was cavorting beneath the parachute.

"Darren Jones! You get out of there!" Miss Collins shouted impatiently.

But Darren Jones was standing right beside Miss Collins, as the rest of the class was only too happy to point out to their agitated teacher. The animated white silk lump turned out to be Zachary.

Poor Miss Collins was understandably embarrassed when she realized her mistake — knowing I had observed the entire incident — and apologized. The mix up gave me a fairly clear idea of the extent of Darren's involvement in the mischief making. Now what to do about it was another matter...until one day toward the end of April.

The slide on the playground had been declared off limits for all students because of a mud puddle at the bottom. To good ol' Zachary though, this was a challenge. So when the teacher wasn't looking, Zachary, followed by Darren Jones, went up the slide. Somehow Zachary managed to land safe and dry on the other side of the puddle. Unfortunately the same could not be said for Darren. He landed flat on his back right in the middle of the puddle. Most of the rest of his day was spent sitting in disgrace in the furnace room — wrapped in a blanket waiting for his clothes to dry — under the supervision of Mr. Grey, the janitor of whom Darren was somewhat in awe.

Talk about the consequences fitting the crime like all those child discipline books recommend! Twenty lectures on the folly of following a bad example couldn't have achieved what that one brief experience did for Darren. He got the message loud and clear!

* * * * *

Bible teaching, of course, was an important part of the program at the academy. We wondered if some of it was a bit heavy, but Andrea seemed to be thriving on it. In fact at the end of the year, she was awarded the Miss Navigator Award — the highest Biblical honor and all around "Good Guy Award" for the entire school! All in all Johnstown Christian Academy was good for our whole family. We all grew spiritually that year, coming to know God in a new and wonderful way as we began to study His word in earnest.

Even Darren acquired a good background in life changing spiritual knowledge and experience. He came home from school one day in an unusually pensive mood as though he had something he wanted to talk about.

Finally he asked me, "You know about the fight?"

"The fight? You mean at school?" I replied uncertainly.

"No, no, not at school. *Everywhere.* God fighting Satan. And Satan fighting God. Even inside us. God wants to be boss and Satan wants to be boss."

"Oh, yes, I know about that fight!" I reassured him.

"You have to choose who's the boss. Even kids like me. We have to choose."

"Yes," I agreed softly, suddenly realizing I was standing on holy ground.

"Well, I chose. Today at school I did. First, I didn't want to. I thought I wanted to be boss of myself. But that's no good! So I said, "Lord Jesus, come into my heart." Not out loud. Inside my head. And He did! Because the Bible says so."

"Holy ground, indeed!" I thought in wonder.

* * * * *

To keep Darren from forgetting what he had learned during the school year at the academy, we thought it would be a good thing if he were tutored during the summer. I had learned in a Friday morning Bible study that a retired teacher named Maggie Powell was willing to take on the task. Not surprisingly, Darren was less than enthusiastic at the prospect of school in the summer and reluctantly went to his first session at Maggie's house. Evidently it wasn't as bad as he had expected because after that first time he usually went off willingly—and sometimes even eagerly—every Tuesday and Thursday morning for his ninety minute sessions with Maggie.

I discovered the curriculum at Maggie's school included more than academics one morning when I arrived to pick Darren up. His face was flushed with excitement and Maggie and her college age daughter, Gina—who was home from college for summer vacation—were both standing behind him...looking exhausted, but triumphant.

"Guess what!" Maggie exclaimed proudly.

I couldn't guess.

"Tell her, Darren," Maggie prompted.

"I can tie shoes?" he said quietly with a questioning wonder in his voice, as though he couldn't quite believe it himself.

"No kidding?" I said, incredulous. "We"ve been trying for years to teach him how to tie his shoes! How did you do it?"

"Actually, Gina did it," Maggie said. "I got to thinking that maybe Darren, being left handed, needed someone left handed to teach him. So I drafted Gina who's also a lefty, and she taught him! Show her Darren."

So Darren plopped down on the floor and untied one of his shoes. Then with great concentration—his tongue wedged between his lips—went to work. Something went wrong with his first attempt, and Gina stepped in to give him a little encouragement. Finally—after another failed attempt and more encouragement from Gina—there was a double bowknot in his shoelace tied with Darren's own two hands!

If he hadn't learned anything else the rest of that summer, this was enough! We were so pleased for Darren... and very grateful to Maggie and Gina.

But happily, Darren also made some academic progress during Maggie's school term that summer... enough, in fact, to inspire Maggie to pen the lovely poem on the next page.

Darren, my student,
Ten years old, thin and frail,
Whom I and others like me have sometimes bored,
Sometimes bewildered,
Because we didn't know what it was like being you.
Yours is a different world
Where things don't come in wholes.
You see a puzzle with pieces missing,
But not always the same pieces.
Yet, stubbornly you keep at it,
Peering nearsightedly, trying to make sense of it all.
Sometimes succeeding, sometimes not—like the rest
of us.
But you know what life's about: "It's love!" you said.
No wonder first grade lessons sometimes missed their
mark.

CHAPTER 36

Answered Prayer

An article on the front page of the *Manning Courier* captured my attention as I sorted the mail one morning. It was about a family in town who had adopted a little Korean orphan girl, and I couldn't get it out of my mind as I went about my work that day. "It's just an interesting, heartwarming story," I kept telling myself — but somehow there was more to it than that.

"Did you see..." Tom started to say that evening.

"...the article in the paper about the family who adopted the Korean orphan?" I interrupted and finished his question without even thinking.

Tom nodded and said, "I can't get it out of my mind."

"Neither can I."

Then after a long silence, Tom put into words what had been in the back of *my* mind all day, "It seems like a message from God. What do you say we check it out...the possibility of us adopting..."

"...a little brother for Darren and an orphan for you?" I finished his thought again. "But yes, I really think we should check it out. Messages from God don't come along every day!"

So, we checked it out.

In the process, I felt the need to examine my personal motives. Did I want to adopt a child because *I* wanted another child to love and take care of, or did I want one as a sort of "playmate" for Darren—as we had gotten Muffin when Andrea wanted a dog?

During this period of soul searching, little faces with dark, solemn eyes captured my attention as I read through the brochure from the agency we were interested in. The Holt International Adoption Agency was a good fit for us since they handled the adoptions of abandoned children in Korea. By now Tom and I were both convinced that if we *did* adopt a child, adopting a Korean orphan was our "calling."

They tugged at my heartstrings too, those little faces. Soon I knew I was *not* looking for a toy for Darren. *I* wanted one of those precious little children—whichever one God chose for us—to love, cherish, nurture and raise to adulthood. I came to want that child with the same passion that I had wanted Andrea and Darren.

Making the decision to adopt was only the first step. There were miles of red tape to contend with, including investigations to determine if we were the kind of people who could be trusted with a child and if our home was suitable. We began to wonder if it would ever come to an end. Finally the call came from the social worker that we had been approved. A few months later, a brown envelope came in the mail with a photo of the child the Holt agency had selected—after much prayer and deliberation—they assured us.

When the envelope arrived, I was home alone. With shaking hands I opened it, pulled out the eight-by-ten photo...and there was Jin Yung Jung, a chubby toddler dressed in Korean clothing, looking up at me solemnly. He was about two and a half—the enclosed letter informed me—and probably of Korean descent.

Tom and I were deeply touched by the sadness etched into his little face, and secretly a bit disappointed in his physical appearance, but the children had a completely different reaction when *they* saw his photo for the first time.

"Yes! Yes! Yes! We want him! That's our brother!" Darren and Andrea chanted in unison over and over again.

Tom and I looked at each other with tears in our eyes. What amazing children we had!

"Jin Yung Jung...is that what we're going to call him?" Andrea wanted to know.

"No, that's a funny name," Darren jumped in. "I don't want him to be called that! He needs a *good* name like...like Aaron."

"Aaron Jones," Tom said thoughtfully. "You know, that does have a good sound to it, doesn't it? We"ll definitely consider that Darren."

But Darren wasn't into considering. His mind was made up and the more the rest of us thought about it, the better *we* liked the name too. Aaron it would be. As to his middle name, we decided on Jin, his Korean first name.

We began to make preparations for the arrival of Aaron Jin Jones, which included Tom selling all of his woodworking tools plus borrowing $5,000 from the bank so we would have enough money to pay all the expenses.

In the meantime something surprising and quite wonderful happened! Darren, who had been a bed wetter his entire life, abruptly *stopped* wetting the bed the *very* night he learned that the wait was over...his earnest prayers for a little brother had been answered!

When he had gone two weeks without an accident, it seemed that it would be safe to invite his friend Eddie Eldridge to a sleepover—something Darren had wanted to do for a long time—but hadn't been able to because of this problem.

And now it would be especially fun because his room had already been rearranged to accommodate his new little brother. At the suggestion of the adoption agency, we'd put a full size mattress on the floor so Aaron would feel more at home while adjusting to his new life since he had always slept on the floor in Korea. And the mattress had to be full size so *someone*—namely his new big brother, Darren—could sleep with him.

The sleepover went well until morning when Eddie burst into our bedroom announcing that Darren had wet the bed.

Oh no! Horrified, I rushed into Darren's room. Sure enough, the bed was wet—but on further investigation I noticed that Darren's pajamas were *not*. What was going on here?! Then I noticed that *Eddie's* pajamas *were* wet.

"Don't feel bad," I comforted Eddie as I rinsed out his pajamas, "it could happen to anyone."

But when Eddie's mother came to pick him up, and I handed her the plastic bag of wet pajamas with a brief explanation, Eddie's mother refused to believe it had happened to Eddie. She insisted that it had to have been Darren!

* * * * *

The time came when we had to decide exactly how we would get Aaron here. We could hire an escort service to bring him to us—or travel to Korea and pick him up ourselves. For a number of reasons, we favored the latter. We felt it would be good for us to visit Korea so we could learn firsthand a bit about our little boy's culture and heritage, plus we felt it would be more welcoming to go ourselves, rather than having him delivered like a package. But for *all* of us to travel overseas was out of the question— it would have been much too expensive. While we were talking it over, Darren insisted that it would be very unfair if *he* didn't get to go—since a little brother was *his* idea. In the end we decided that *I* should be the one to go—and my mother, bless her heart, volunteered to accompany me at her own expense. I spent the better part of a week searching for the most reasonable airfare. Aaron could have flown for free if he was only two, but because he was two and a half, I was told we would have to pay the full adult fare for him. We hadn't counted on this and with our budget already stretched pretty thin, I made a last-ditch effort and called the President of Japan Airlines himself to explain our situation and make my appeal. And it paid off! With special permission from the airline president himself, Aaron could fly home with me for free!

On the eve of my departure, I began having second—and third and fourth—thoughts about this whole undertaking. I hadn't even left yet and here I was already feeling homesick and apprehensive—not only about the long trip, but the whole idea of adoption was creeping in. What if...? What if things didn't go right? Not just the trip, but after the adoption? We had thought it all over and prayed about it again and again and this *seemed* to be what God wanted us to do. But what if we had made a mistake? What if we had misunderstood? These doubts were both sobering and scary beyond words now that it was actually about to happen!

I spent most of the night praying and reminding myself of all the times God had helped us even when we hadn't been sensible enough to ask Him for help—unable to see the help He was giving us. I would just have to trust Him to take care of everything. If this was what He wanted for us, surely He would supply what we needed, no matter how inadequate and scared I felt at the moment. Then I once again remembered the story of the man who saw only one set of footprints in the sand and accused God of forsaking him in his time of greatest need—only to find out that God *had* been there guiding him—in fact *carrying* him through his most difficult tribulations...so I put my trust in God and finally, in the early morning hours, sleep came.

Thanks to the comfort my last waking thoughts brought me, I was feeling remarkably well the next morning in spite of the mostly sleepless night I had spent praying and worrying. It was a lovely June morning—perfect for traveling—as we headed off to the international airport in Stanton. I pushed away the vestiges of my lingering doubts, so I could revel in the exhilaration I was beginning to feel at the prospect of my upcoming adventure!

We arrived at the airport just in time to meet Mother's plane from Florida. Then after a brief flurry of activity, my mother and I were flying off to Korea where the next chapter of our lives would begin to unfold.

CHAPTER 37

Orphan No More!

The taxi ride into Seoul was a wild one with traffic coming and going in all directions at a breakneck speed. My first impression of the city was that of an immense sea of round, tan faces ebbing and flowing around us at slightly below my eye level. People, people everywhere!

Late into the warm and rainy afternoon, we checked into the guest house where the adoption agency had made reservations for us. Air conditioning would have been most welcome, but a small freestanding fan that appeared to be of 1930's vintage was the only relief from the heat. After resting a bit and freshening up, we ventured out into the steamy evening air to find a place to eat.

There were plenty of Western style restaurants, but in the spirit of adventure we had our hearts set on eating in a restaurant with a Korean atmosphere. We strolled along the still busy street—eagerly taking in the sights, sounds and smells of this huge city that couldn't seem to make up its mind whether to be modern or ancient—while we searched for the perfect restaurant. We wandered past shopping arcades and department stores that would have blended comfortably into any large city back home. Wedged between little shops bulging with everything from lacquerware to costumed dolls and set back from the street in a park-like setting, we admired a palatial tile-roofed building—a temple, perhaps?—that looked as though it had been there forever.

We came at last to a promising looking restaurant which would provide the taste of Korea we were hoping for. A baffling array of dishes was set before us—and although we could identify some of the contents—most left us guessing. It was a fascinating culinary adventure, but in the end we admitted that true Korean food might take just a little getting used to.

It hadn't occurred to me to find out just what time the adoption agency office opened, so I decided that after we had finished breakfast would be about right.

Boy, I was wrong! Although there appeared to be some activity inside, the door was locked, so we sat down on the steps outside and waited. And waited. Fortunately, it wasn't raining although it looked like it could at any moment without half trying.

Finally after nearly an hour, a smiling young Korean woman opened the door and invited us in. By this time I was feeling a bit piqued at having to wait so long. But my impatience rapidly disappeared when I learned that the members of the staff spent the first hour of each work day in prayer regarding the proper placement of each child in their care.

The agency director outlined our schedule. This afternoon we would meet Jin Yung Jung at the orphanage, which was about an hour's bus ride from Seoul. From the orphanage, we would all go to the Baby Home in Seoul and spend five days alone with him getting acquainted. At the end of each day, he would be returned to the Home. Then if all went well—and I had no doubt that it would—the final arrangements would be made and the three of us would be on our way back home.

That trip to the orphanage was one of the longest hours I have ever spent. I was reeling topsy-turvy on an emotional roller coaster ride that would lift me up, up, up in a feeling of joyful anticipation, plunge me down into a dizzying spiral of despairing apprehension the next moment, and then before I could blink it would be whisking me back up, up, up again.

We got off the bus at a lovely wooded area in the mountains. Set back a bit from the road among the trees was the orphanage—a two story, peach-colored stucco building.

I was glad that I was on the up side of happy anticipation as we were greeted by the matron of the home. On the way to meet Jin Yung Jung the matron explained that the children were divided into "families of eight" under the care of one adult and each family shared one large room.

When we stepped into the room that was Jin Yung's home, all the toddlers came with surprising readiness to greet us. I searched their little faces for the one familiar one. And then I spied him—holding back all by himself on the other side of the room—a little butterball of a fellow looking very solemn, scared and forlorn.

Could he actually understand that he was going to leave this place - up rooted again from the home he had known for only six months—and be taken by these two strange looking ladies to the other side of the world? It didn't seem possible, but I wondered.

My first instinct was to run to him, gather him up in my arms, give him a big hug and then reassure him everything was going to be all right. But I knew that would probably frighten him even more, so I restrained myself. It would be better to wait and let him come to me.

The "parent" of the family was a woman that I thought was surprisingly old to be taking care of eight children this young. She said something to Jin Yung in Korean then held out her hand, but he did not respond. It was almost as though he had not heard her, even though he was looking directly at her. So I went over to him, took his hand and gently drew him to our side of the room. Still he hung back, turning his head away from me.

"Is he afraid of us?" I asked the matron.

"I think he is just very shy," she answered.

Finally, I went over to him again, lifted him up and hugged him as I had been longing to do. This was greeted with much resistance including squirming and pushing to get away.

The matron, trying to make things better, said something in Korean, which only made them worse. Suddenly the child in my arms became a little tornado— screaming, twisting and flinging himself about—struggling as though for his very life. It turned out that she had only said the lady holding him was his new mother. We found out some time later that he had been abused by his biological mother so he had a good reason to react with such panic…but no one knew that at the time.

Needless to say, it was not a pleasant afternoon nor would any of the following days be filled with happy memories of getting acquainted. Although he would cry when we brought him back to the home each afternoon, he also cried when we took him each morning.

He simply was not responsive to any of our efforts to be friends and have a good time. The best time we had was when we took him to a Western-style restaurant for dinner. My mother and I were both impressed and very touched when he sat waiting quietly—with hands folded and head bowed—while the food was set before him. But after the blessing was over, one thing became quite obvious—Jin Yung liked to eat! If the food was strange to him—and it very likely was—that certainly didn't keep him from enjoying it.

Typically, Koreans have coarse, thick, very black hair, but here sat this little butterball with pimples on his face and *thin reddish brown hair*. Sadly, this pointed to a diet severely devoid of sufficient nutrients, so it was wonderful to see him enjoying the food. But he still hadn't warmed up even one tiny bit to his new mother or grandmother. As time passed my emotions ebbed lower and lower. A disturbing suspicion had formed and was haunting me.

"Mother, I think he's retarded!" I finally blurted out to my mom.

She looked at me, startled. "Surely they would have told you...wouldn't they?"

"Well, I would think so, but..."

I decided right then that I was going to ask the social worker point blank before things proceeded any further.

The poor social worker looked quite shocked when I told her what I suspected. "Certainly not!" she exclaimed. "We would have told you, of course." I suggested that I would like to talk with the doctor who had recently examined Jin Yung in connection with the adoption.

When I spoke with the doctor, her tone was not quite as positive as the social worker's had been. "Oh, no, I don't think he's retarded," she had said with a sigh. "He's not the smartest child in the world, but I don't think he's retarded."

"And what if he is?" I confronted myself after meeting with the doctor.

But...I already had one retarded child. And as much as I adored him, did I really want to take on another? Should I? Would it be fair to Darren? My emotional roller coaster was hurtling me down into the very pits of despair. But then I reminded myself that *this* was the child we felt God had *chosen for us*. In consideration of that, was I even free to make the choice *not* to adopt him? I very much needed to talk this over with my husband. It certainly wasn't a decision I could make alone.

When I called home that afternoon, the phone rang for such a long time that I was starting to get worried when it dawned on me that it was about two o"clock in the morning there. Definitely not a great time to discuss life-changing decisions with Tom—or anyone else, for that matter.

Finally he answered sleepily. "Everything all right?" he asked when he heard my voice.

I explained why I was calling, but I had the feeling I was trying to communicate with a brick wall. Tom didn't seem to be grasping the seriousness of the situation. His response was that since I was there and he wasn't, the final decision was up to me. *We might as well have been talking about whether or not I should bring home pork chops for dinner,* I thought helplessly. Eventually he did offer a positive thought...*hadn't God put this adoption in motion?* Then it must be what was supposed to happen, so go ahead and bring him home.

Well, that settled it. But when I crawled into bed that night I was still feeling desolate and ill-equipped for the problems that might lay ahead. But wait! I was not without resources! After all, as Tom had said, this was God's concern too, wasn't it?

Another retarded child. I stared into the semi-darkness for a long time, playing out in my mind the outcome of this decision. No, another retarded child was not *my* choice. But this child *was* God's choice. And who was I to dispute that? Retarded or not he was now ours.

Surprisingly and inexplicably, as soon as we got on the plane, Jin Yung became a far different child from the withdrawn, frightened one we had taken from the Baby Home.

After a long 14 hour flight, the plane set down at the Stanton airport in early evening. Jin Yung had fallen asleep about a half hour before arrival and now he was in such a stupor that heavy as he was, I carried him off the plane and into the terminal. The minute we came down the ramp, we were met with flashing lights and what seemed like a dozen excited children. Tom had brought along his camera to record this momentous occasion. The dozen children turned out to be only Andrea and Darren, jumping up and down wildly and squealing greetings to their new little brother.

Jin Yung sleepily endured all the hubbub and allowed Tom to carry him to the car.

"I still don't know if my suspicions are right or not," I said, following close behind.

"What?" Tom paused, turning his head in my direction.

"You know—what I called about. You do remember my phone call, don't you?"

"Oh, that. We"ll manage," he said calmly.

We had scarcely gotten Jin Yung strapped into the new child safety seat between Darren and Andrea before he dropped off to sleep again, and he barely woke up when we tucked him into his own bed in the room he would share with Darren.

"When's he gonna wake up?" Darren wanted to know, apparently not the least bit sleepy. "I want to play with him and show him my toys."

We had a little trouble convincing Darren that everything would have to wait until morning. We hoped he wouldn't be disappointed when morning came.

He wasn't. We woke to the sound of giggling coming from the boys' room early the next morning. We tiptoed down the hall and peeked in. Darren, and now Aaron, as Darren began to call his new brother, were sitting side by side on the floor surrounded by the contents of the toy box. From the look and sound of things, we were hard put to say who was having the most fun—big brother or little brother.

We never knew what happened to that little boy that I had been ready to label retarded. From that first morning on, there was no longer any doubt as to Aaron's intelligence.

When he arrived in America, Aaron did not speak English and for the first two weeks he was quite unhappy that his new family did not speak Korean. We knew only one Korean phrase—"Don't cry!"

Soon, however, he was beginning to understand English and communicate with no problem whatsoever.

Darren taught him to count up to twelve—as far as Darren himself knew—and by the time Aaron was three he was singing and reciting his ABC's quite flawlessly. The doctor in Korea had labeled him "not the smartest kid in the world." But after Aaron had been with us only a few months, we weren't so sure. Maybe we had a genius on our hands!

Praise be to God! That whole adoption experience had drawn our entire family closer to Christ. *"Whoever receives one little child like this in My name receives Me"* (Matthew 18:5).

CHAPTER 38

Another Prayer, Another Blessing

It was time to finish up the one year evaluation and paperwork for Aaron's adoption, and he and I sat in the little waiting room at the Holt Adoption agency for the final interview. Scattered about were picture albums of children needing homes. I leafed through the albums, my heart touched with sadness that there were so many children without the love of a family.

"Ready for another one?" Michelle, the Holt agency director, asked as she called us into her office, noting my interest in the albums.

"Ah...no...just browsing," I replied. But that wasn't exactly the truth. Actually now that Darren had gotten the little brother he had prayed for, Andrea was thinking it was *her* turn. Not that she didn't enjoy Aaron—he was her joy and delight and she was a little mother to him. "But how about a sister for me?" she kept asking.

Michelle didn't pursue the subject and the final interview for Aaron's adoption passed with flying colors. Aaron was definitely ours and we went home to celebrate with a special dinner.

About two months later, Michelle called. The agency had a little girl who desperately needed a home. I shuddered as Michelle filled me in on just how desperately. She wanted to know if the Jones family would consider being put on the list of families that could take her.

At dinner that evening, I told the rest of the family about Michelle's call and the girl who was in need of a home. Her name was Celia. She was eleven years old and originally from the Philippines. When she was only four days old, she had been left on the doorstep of a rich single woman who lived with her parents. The woman, whom Celia called Auntie, adopted Celia and Auntie's parents would take care of her while Auntie traveled with her business.

When Celia was just five, Grandpa and Grandma died and because Auntie was unable to care for her, she was sent to Texas to live with Auntie's sister who was married to a medical doctor. Celia was very unhappy to leave Auntie and began acting out her unhappiness in disruptive behavior. After only two years, that family gave Celia to another sister, who kept her for a year and then passed her on to a fourth sister who lived with a nephew in San Francisco. Celia and that sister didn't get along and Celia's behavior went from bad to worse. Finally she ran away from home and now she was in the custody of the State of California. Not a very positive picture. Still…We all decided that this was a matter for prayer. We would let God open or close the doors.

In mid-April I phoned Michelle and asked that we be put on the list of families that would take Celia.

Two days later the call came. We had been chosen to take Celia. Could we pick her up in California at the end of April?

"*This* year?" I asked in shock.

Obviously there was no time to worry or change our minds now. I stayed up late that night putting together a scrapbook of our family to send to Celia, trying to include pictures of anything I thought would help put her at ease about her new family—our house, the pink flowered room with a sleeping loft Tom had built that she would share with Andrea, and the activities we enjoyed.

What must it be like for an eleven year old to be making such a change after all the other upheavals she had been through? How could we help her understand that God had planned this change and now she would belong forever to our family? Help, Lord!

I traveled alone this time to bring our new family member home. I had not yet seen *one* picture of her. Most of the four hour flight I spent praying and thinking about what to say to our new daughter. "Lord, please put the right words in my mouth," I kept pleading silently.

I was met at the Oakland airport by a kindly, middle-aged woman holding the hand of a very dark-skinned young girl with a Dutch boy hair cut. The girl's frilly white dress seemed to be trying very hard to make up for her tomboy look but it wasn't succeeding very well.

Hurriedly the social worker introduced us, saying she had to move her car so it wouldn't be towed away and would be back as soon as possible. Then she disappeared.

Celia and I were left alone staring at each other. Once again I prayed for the right words, opened my mouth and out came, "Celia, you are so pretty!"

A broad smile lit up the girl's face and I knew that— whether they were completely accurate or not—those were the right words. Then I couldn't help asking, "Celia, are you as scared as I am?"

Celia nodded vigorously and we hugged each other. From then on our conversation flourished until at last the social worker returned, out of breath and apologizing for taking so long. She had gotten caught in a traffic jam. She was surprised and pleased to discover her young charge and me visiting like long lost friends.

"Now I *know* Celia will be all right!" she announced happily. "She's never talked to anyone right away like this."

The return flight gave us plenty of opportunity to continue getting acquainted and we didn't waste a second of it. During our conversation on the plane ride home, I had asked if she went to church.

"Oh yes, every Sunday! I don't think I have ever missed a week!" she replied quickly.

"Do you know some stories from the Bible?" I inquired.

"At the moment, I can't think of one," she hedged.

"How about Moses?" I had asked.

"Moses who?" she responded.

Hmmmm…well, maybe something from the New Testament. "Do you remember the story about Jesus turning water into wine in the New Testament?" I tried again.

"New Testament? What is that?" had been Celia's response.

Evidently she had gone to church but was not taught the Bible.

As the plane circled for a landing, the subject of Celia's name came up.

"Am I pronouncing it correctly?" I wondered.

"Yes…"she said, frowning, "but I hate it. It means chair in Filipino and I hate it. My real name is Maria Celia."

"Would you rather be called Maria?" I asked. "Now is the perfect time to change it."

"Oh, yes, call me Maria!" was the happy response. And so, Maria she was ever after.

* * * * *

It was May and there was still a month of the school year left. We decided that the best choice for Maria was the Christian School. We feared that in public school she would end up at the bottom of the barrel for friends. At least for now she needed a small caring place that would nurture her and make sure that she made the right kind of friends.

So the first of May Maria was off to school on the Academy van with the other children. Though we felt quite comfortable about her social well being, how well she would fit in academically at a Christian school might be another matter.

Maria entered into her new school adventure with enthusiasm, coming home with stories of meeting new friends and even an occasional learning experience.

Then about two weeks later, she bounded into the kitchen, "Mom, our Bible class is studying the Book of Revelation and tomorrow we have a test. Can you help me?"

Remembering our conversation on the plane, Maria had never heard of Moses or the New Testament and now she was having a test on Revelation? She needed prayer!

Not being extremely versed on that book of the Bible myself, I suggested that Andrea and Maria sit at the dinning room table and study that complicated book of the Bible. Soon Andrea realized that most of what she was saying was far over Maria's head. She thought how could Maria understand the Book of Revelation when she doesn't understand the basic life of Christ? Andrea then decided to go through the Book of John to explain the basics.

The girls studied long after two young girls should be up on a school night. Finally, I shooed them off to bed. When they were finally tucked into the loft for the night, I climbed the little ladder so I could lean my elbows on the pink carpet where the two mattresses lay and prayed with them. We prayed about the test and then Maria asked if she could be "born again" as it says in the Book of John. "Maria do you understand that being 'born again' means born of the Spirit?" I asked. "Do you want Jesus Christ to be your Lord and Savior?" Yes, I want to have Jesus as my "boss" and save me from my own sinful self."

And Andrea said, "Now I know why she is in our family."

The next afternoon Maria came bursting in from school looking like she had just won a million dollars.

"Mom! Mom!" she called, "We had a three page typewritten test and I only got *one* wrong!"

Best of all, through the study with Andrea of the "Revelation of Jesus Christ," as the book introduces itself, Maria came to know Him personally as her Savior.

She came to us a tomboy, plain and awkward with many problems that had to be worked through; today, by the grace of God she is a beautiful, responsible young wife, a good mother not only to her own children, but to needy ones wherever she goes.

CHAPTER 39

Just Me and Dad

One day an ad in the newspaper caught Tom's attention: **FOR SALE — Used go cart.**

While Andrea, Aaron and Maria all had school friends and activities to fill up their spare time, Darren still needed special attention and Tom thought a go cart would fill the bill nicely as one of those "just me and Dad" activities that Darren seemed to especially enjoy. So Tom went to check out the go-cart, and it turned out to be very used indeed, but the price was right so he bought it. Powered by a Briggs and Stratton motor, it had gas and brake pedals, could reach a speed of 25-30mph and would serve their purposes just fine!

With much time and effort — under Darren's eager and watchful eye — Tom coaxed the go-cart into good running condition. He built a plywood seat in the back over the wheels for himself, so he could operate the accelerator and the brake while Darren sat in the driver's seat learning to steer.

The parking lot of an abandoned grocery store made a safe and roomy space to drive the go-cart, and before long Darren was steering by himself. Orange cones set up as an obstacle course helped Darren improve his skill. At first he wiped out a good number of cones, but with practice he became quite the expert. Then with Dad still sitting on the back, he mastered the gas pedal. After that came the brake — but that was rarely used. Darren had learned to be a cautious driver so that very little braking was necessary. And what a thrill it was when he was able to take off — putt-putting round and round the parking lot — all by himself!

The go-cart mastered, Darren began to eye the moped Andrea had recently outgrown. He had long ago taught himself to ride a two wheeler, but it would take a lot more know how to ride a moped, but he had done so well with the go cart that Tom decided they could give it a try. Again Tom made a back seat for himself, this time by tying a rolled up blanket on the luggage carrier of the moped. With Dad's hands over his, Darren slowly mastered the twist grip accelerator and brake levers on the handlebars. His thumb even found the horn button, which made riding the moped, a special delight for him.

But his first attempts at riding solo were disastrous. He was reluctant to start off with enough speed to balance the moped and he didn't feel confident enough to lift his feet off the ground. Eventually he was able to take off by himself, but he preferred riding on the sidewalk rather than the street. Thank goodness we were blessed with very kind neighbors who never complained. They realized what an achievement this was for a nearly blind rider. They would even encourage him and watch over him to make sure the little kids stayed out of his way.

One day as Tom was watching from a block away, Darren and the moped flipped off the sidewalk and flew through the air, landing on the grass. Tom ran up the block not knowing what he would find when he reached the site of the accident. As he got closer, he saw that the sidewalk had been broken up in large chunks and piled up for removal — and immediately knew the cause of the crash. Darren with his limited vision hadn't seen the danger.

He was lying on the grass with one leg caught under the moped — its motor still running. Tom shut off the motor and righted the moped. Everything looked okay. No broken bones, not even any spilled gas. Darren picked himself up and other than grass stains, a couple of bruises and a very bruised ego he was just fine. Although he became even more cautious after this incident, we were glad it didn't discourage him from riding the moped. He needed to participate in "normal kid" activities and know there was more to life than watching TV all day.

CHAPTER 40

Making Big Waves

Darren attended the Christian school for three years, kindergarten for one year and first grade for two. He loved the school, the kids and the teachers. He had learned phonics and was reading—very slowly—at the second grade level. Now we felt it would be a good time to get him back in the Special Ed class in public school. Surely, with this evidence that he could learn, they would be required to provide an *educable* classroom for him where he would receive academic instruction. Several staff IEP meetings later—the staff including the superintendent of schools, the psychologist, a social worker and teachers—to our dismay, we were informed that Darren was being placed in the *trainable* classroom. We were frustrated beyond words!

Besides there being no academic program, the classroom itself was disappointing to say the least. It occupied the basement of an old elementary building and the message was clear—leftovers were good enough for *"those kids."* And when I visited Darren's class, I discovered that the floor was bare concrete—and with the continual scraping of steel chairs the noise level was unbelievable. How could anyone—to say nothing of learning disabled students—learn anything in such a loud and disruptive environment? I suggested that the installation of draperies and carpeting would help, but spending money to improve the handicapped classroom didn't seem to be very high on anyone's list.

Determined to do *something*, I requested an audiologist test. This showed the noise level to be even higher than anyone had thought. Surely now they would do something, so I requested a staff meeting.

Everyone was there at the start of this meeting except the superintendent of schools. He came in late and signed in on the official form while everyone else was focused on the discussion. He didn't contribute one word, then got up and walked out before the end of the meeting. I wondered what was going on with him?

The sign in sheet revealed that he had signed in, not as the superintendent of schools, but as a representative of the County Taxpayers Association. I never did know why, but I wondered if he ever signed in as a county taxpayer at a meeting to spend money on the football or basketball teams? He actually had no right to be at this personal and confidential meeting as a taxpayer or private citizen—yet this was the same person who had pointed out the power of "the law" when we had met with him before we moved to Manning. Was there any hope of working with him in improving the educational environment of the handicapped as the law required?

We doubted it but we persevered and continued to request IEP meetings, trying to get Darren what he needed— and what the law required.

Armed with the audiologist report, we formally presented our request for draperies and carpeting to the school board. It was scheduled to be discussed at the next school board meeting. As it happened, on that particular night another important issue was to be discussed so the meeting room was packed. And surprisingly, when they got to our request, it was approved after only a short discussion.

"There! I hope that keeps her quiet for a while!" one of the board members remarked loudly, not realizing that I was present at the meeting.

After murmurs rippled around the room that I was present, they swiftly moved on to other business.

Unfortunately, it seemed as if we were gaining a reputation for disturbing the waters of the Manning School System. Surely there were others who cared about the learning needs of the handicapped—but where were they? No one else seemed to be willing to make waves. But how were conditions going to be improved if no one challenged them? We had been instructed to be advocates for our children at a seminar on assertiveness training for parents of disabled children. Even though the laws are on the books, they often need to be challenged before they are put into effect.

At our request, the closed circuit TV that Darren used in the Christian school had been transferred to his classroom in Manning, but apparently it was not being used. Neither were we seeing any homework, even though we asked for it repeatedly. As the year progressed, Darren achieved so little in school it amounted to practically nothing—and his behavior became worse and worse. What to do?

* * * * *

Although our time in Manning was marred by all the difficulties we had concerning Darren's education, we do have some fond memories of our time there. There is a certain camaraderie in small towns that just can't be duplicated anywhere. One event stands out fondly in our memories and exemplifies the happier side of the coin. We had decided to attend the first Citywide Lip Sync Contest. Five hundred people had packed into the Manning Auditorium and everyone had a wonderful time. On our way back home from the show there was excitement in the car as we all laughed and joked about the people we knew that had been on stage. Then Dad announced to us all, "We're going to enter next month's performance. We"ll lip sync to a song from the 50's—*Yakity Yak, Don't Talk Back.*

It fits our family perfectly and there will be parts for all of us!"

"Oh, no!" Andrea and I said in unison with embarrassment. But by the time our station wagon was pulling into our driveway, we were already talking excitedly about which part we would play and what costume we could put together. And a month later, when the event was held again, the Jones family was ready!

Clad in black leather and wearing shades, Maria introduced the song — dancing out onto the stage "playing" an old saxophone — minus the mouthpiece — with such enthusiasm that the audience thought she was actually playing it at first. Throughout the song she danced and played like a real pro — adding the cool factor to our little presentation.

Four year old Aaron brought the house down again as he swaggered out next — lip syncing with mop and bucket in hand. Andrea — looking groovy dressed in hippie garb — threw out the stuffed cat, brought in the stuffed dog, then began to mop the floor…mimicking the lyrics of the song with great timing. Darren was break dancing while Dad scolded him for not taking out the trash and I was shouting orders for Maria to do the laundry and Andrea to come in on time…not too much out of character for me. And each time the lyric "*Yakety Yak!*" would come up — right on cue Andrea, Darren and Aaron would all stop their antics and raise their fists or mops or brooms and shake them at us as if they were arguing with their nerdy parents — then Tom and I would lip sync the phrase "*Don't talk back!*" and waggle our fingers at them in reprimand!

Everyone played their part brilliantly and we all danced off stage at the end of the song to the happy sounds of the thunderous applause, raucous cheers and loud whistles of our appreciative audience.

We never could agree which part of this family adventure was the most fun — Mom and Dad dressing like nerds (which didn't take a great deal of effort —

especially for Dad—but that's another story!), the creative costumes that the kids wore, the many hours of practice in our backyard to get the timing just right, the nervous excitement of the performance itself, standing on stage winning and receiving the $100 first prize, or seeing the photo of our whole family on stage on the front cover of Tom's company newsletter.

But we did all agree that it had been a wonderful family adventure and we have a copy of our performance on tape to prove it that we still enjoy watching to this day. And for me it is a special joy to watch that tape and see Darren up there with us, playing his part so well that unless you knew our story, you would never suspect that he was legally blind or mentally disabled. He looks just like any other kid having fun with his family!

It's really a shame the Manning school officials could never understand that *those kids* can be pretty normal and accomplish amazing things when they are in a supportive environment surrounded by people who genuinely care.

CHAPTER 41

The Best Laid Plans

Everywhere we turned, we came up against a brick wall. Was it time to do something really drastic? Maybe we could find a suitable program for Darren in another city. Corporate changes at Tom's job had made a change of location possible, so I began visiting different school districts to see what was available elsewhere.

I was impressed by what I saw in a few districts. A very promising program was in place in Baldwin, a city larger than Manning and about fifty miles away. In regard to Tom's work, Baldwin would actually be a more convenient place for us to live than Manning. The more we investigated, the better things looked. Only one problem — selling our house in the small town of Manning. This was during the recession of the '80's when interest rates on mortgages ran high. Not a good time to sell or buy a house, but we decided to take the plunge. It took much longer than we would have liked and we got less for it than we had hoped — but we were finally free to move!

About the same time as the house was being sold, we bought a very nice, but used, full sized van. No more crowded trips to Florida, visiting their aunt and uncle every year in that old station wagon. Now all six of us had our own special seats. Mom and Dad were in the front, of course. Andrea and Maria were in the middle seats and Darren and Aaron shared the roomy seat in the back, which, if need be, could be pulled out into a bed for naps. I especially liked the fact that I could walk all the way to the back to settle any arguments.

When we brought it home, everyone was excited and we were all looking it over when Andrea made the comment, "It's plush enough to be a living room during the day and convert into a bedroom at night."

Aaron's mind went on overload with all the talk of our house being sold and the van converting from a living room to a bedroom with ease. Being especially skilled in the *whys* and *what fors* of a four year old he asked me, "What if we have to use the toilet?"

"Oh, we"ll just stop at a gas station," was my answer.

"What about all our clothes?" he wanted to know.

"We"ll take suitcases," I replied.

Common sense answers if you're thinking about taking a trip…right? But as Andrea, Maria and Darren got more and more excited about moving to a larger town and a bigger house, Aaron became more concerned and depressed. Finally one day he blurted out, "Mom, I don't want to live in a *van*. I want to live in a *house!*"

Obviously he had missed the conversation about buying a new house in Baldwin and had thought we were planning on selling our house and becoming wandering vagabonds — living in our new van! With a short explanation to clarify that we would also have a new house to live in between trips, we were once again all traveling in the same direction and eager to move on to the next phase of our lives.

The house we found in Baldwin suited us perfectly. It was in a pleasant neighborhood on a cul de sac — no busy traffic to worry about — and it had a beautiful backyard that looked like a park. Darren's school would be just two blocks away and two blocks in the other direction was a public swimming pool. We were all excited about moving to our wonderful new home. At sixteen, Andrea swam like a fish now and was looking forward to applying for a position as a lifeguard at the nearby pool, while Maria was looking forward to trying out for lead soprano at the new high school Andrea and she would be attending.

We rented a U-Haul—during what turned out to be the hottest days in July—and made the many trips back and forth necessary to move our family of six. Not a fun job, but we all agreed that the advantages of this move made it all worthwhile.

As soon as the school was open for new registrations, we eagerly set up a meeting to develop Darren's new IEP.

That was when our new world came crashing down on us. Darren, now fourteen, was *too old* to be enrolled in this school!

Too old? After all the time we had spent carefully investigating our options to choose the perfect school? We couldn't believe it! How could this be? We had already sold our house in Manning and moved to Baldwin—and everyone already loved it there. Now what? It took us several minutes to recover and control the anger we felt that we hadn't been informed about this before and then to exhaust all questions and inquiries as to other possibilities.

The staff at the school couldn't understand the devastation we felt. In their minds there was a very simple solution. Darren could be bused to K.B. Roberts, a segregated school for the handicapped in Stanton, about 30 minutes away. Some eighty buses took students to and from the surrounding areas each day.

A *segregated* school! Oh, no! Admittedly mainstreaming didn't work well for Darren -as we had discovered from past experience—but isolating him from the world with *only* mentally handicapped children to interact with surely wasn't the answer either! Plus we didn't like the idea of his being bused that far every day.

Reluctantly, we decided to give it a try. What choice did we have?

Rather than sending Darren on the bus the first day, I chose to drive him to school, hoping I could meet the teachers and observe some classes. I was surprised and pleased with what I saw. As I entered the school, a huge sign read "**RESPECT OTHERS.**" Tom and I had recently been in another public school that promoted the self-esteem concept with a gigantic sign reading "**RESPECT YOURSELF.**" Tom said, "When I was in school in the 50's we were taught to respect others...that's what the sign would have read." Now we were pleasantly surprised to know that Darren would be taught to respect others, to value others, to love others as opposed to schools that promote the self-esteem, self-worth, self-love and the gospel of self. Loving other than self, not being selfish is what Jesus taught in His two greatest commandants. "...you shall love the Lord your God with all your heart, and with all your soul and with all your mind ... you shall love your neighbor as you do yourself." Matt. 22:37,40 (AMP). Jesus knew that we already love and focus on ourselves too much and that by loving, esteeming and respecting others Darren would experience the joy of caring for and giving to others.

The overall program was quite different from what we had expected. The teachers I met seemed dedicated, kind and genuinely interested in Darren. There was an extensive sports program, including a swimming team and practice pool, basketball, track, baseball and on and on—everything a regular school had and more.

At the beginning, however, Darren was not happy with his new school and showed his resentment by not talking for two days—quite a switch for this boy who was rarely ever quiet. Before long, however, he was back to his old talkative self and actually enjoying the busy routine of changing classes, just like in regular high school.

Darren had always loved sports and enjoyed participating in various competitions in Special Olympics from year to year. Now he was on the high school swim team. With his long arms, big hands and slender body his best events were freestyle (the American crawl) and backstroke and he collected his share of ribbons and medals.

As a first place winner at the local level in Special Olympics, he was thrilled to travel with the school swim team to the State Meet, an experience that promised to surpass even the glory of ribbons and medals. It would be a long, wonderful weekend of staying in college dorms, just like a college student. How exciting!

Tom had to work the day of the meet, so I drove up by myself. Hundreds of students from all over the state were gathered for the event. I marveled at the planning it must have taken to organize it. While I was waiting for the meet to begin, I viewed with respect the Olympic sized indoor pool where the competition would be held. It would have accommodated *three* of the practice pools at home. Could Darren even make it across that enormous span of water—let alone *win*?

The sound of excitement rippled through the crowd in the bleachers and echoed off the walls of the enormous open space and the thrill of anticipation was heavy in the air.

And then the first group to swim lined up on the opposite side of the pool—four sturdy athletic guys—and Darren...skinny, long legged, slightly hunched over. My first thought was that he didn't have a prayer, but I prayed anyway. My second thought was that it would only be by the grace of God that he would even make it to the other side!

The starting gun echoed through the huge room and they were off! Amazingly, they were all neck and neck to the half way mark. Then, by some miracle, Darren's slender form *pulled ahead*. Then a little farther ahead. Never had I seen him swim like that! His endurance was incredible. About four breaths across the entire pool and it was over.

Darren had won the Gold! Darren Jones had won the Gold!!!

I could scarcely contain myself and the ear to ear smile on Darren's face told me he was no less thrilled. If only the rest of the family could have been there to see the radiance on Darren's face and celebrate the happiness of this moment with him too!

A frightening incident occurred the next morning — the first of two such incidents caused by his defective eyesight — and left a little blot on that weekend for Darren. Heading down for breakfast on the elevators with some twenty fellow athletes and their chaperones, he got lost. Because of his undependable eyesight, he didn't realize that his group had gotten off the elevator until he suddenly found himself among strangers riding up and down with no idea where his friends were or where he should get off.

After a very long scary time, he finally did meet up with his group in the right place, but the telling of it afterward was done in a shaky voice.

One of Darren's most valuable experiences at K.B. Roberts was being a buddy and helper to a younger student. This was part of a student's training in respecting others. Darren's charge was a little boy named Isaac who was wheelchair bound and at a lower level mentally than Darren. He took his responsibility of being a friend and helper to Isaac very seriously, and every day we heard about what was going on with the two of them. Before our eyes we could see our son maturing, discovering that the secret to true joy and long lasting happiness was respecting and helping others!

Though K.B. Roberts was not our first choice for Darren, we are now very grateful that God overruled our plans and brought it into his life. What a blessing!

And there were many other blessings we discovered that came with living in Baldwin. The Fourth of July was a special occasion for us since it was also Maria's birthday, but it was a very special day for our neighborhood too. All the neighbors on our cul de sac…about 30 kids and adults…always paraded around the circle and up the street. At the beginning of every July bikes were decorated and instruments not played all year were dragged out of the closets, dusted off and tuned up. When the big day came, kids lined up in their red, white and blue outfits and our neighbor Bill Thomas — baton and cassette radio in hand — would lead the parade marching to the sound of The Star Spangled Banner.

Then came the neighborhood water fight and it wasn't just for kids. Everyone prepared buckets of water balloons, filled squirt guns — and some even armed themselves with garden hoses — but none were as prepared as the Jones family on Maria's special Sweet Sixteen birthday. We had approached some friends on the fire department prior to this celebration asking if they would like to bring a fire truck and be on our side in the neighborhood water fight. Of course they couldn't promise…but as if on cue, just as the water fight was getting underway, around the corner and down our hill came a big red fire truck.

"Surprise! Now who wants to be on *our* side?" shouted the Jones family as the fire truck pulled up in front of our house. The firemen were wonderful! They had even brought along their own kids to join the all day fun. Soon after hooking up the hoses to the hydrant there was water arching criss-cross over the circle and the firemen gave all the kids a chance to hold the hose and feel the power surging through their hands. No one cared what side they were on now. All the children got to climb on the fire truck, everyone got wet — and we *all* won! And best of all, Maria had a very unique and memorable sixteenth birthday!

It turned out to be another of the many special fun family times the Jones kids remember when they revisit their childhood memories.

CHAPTER 42

Shooting from the Hip

Sitting a child in front of the TV provides an easy kid sitter but does very little to stimulate them either physically or mentally. It takes a bit of effort on the parents' part to introduce children to alternative pastimes. To come up with other activities that *Darren* could be involved in was always a special challenge for us. With everything we did or wanted to do as a family, the question of how Darren could be involved was always a consideration. We had made a point of having one-on-one activities with each child but we also set aside times like Sunday after church for events the whole family could participate in together.

The guys at Tom's job were into guns and were always talking about shooting and hunting, but we were city folks who knew nothing about guns and had never been hunting. So when Tom suggested that a great family project would be to learn about firearms and how to shoot guns, I was hesitant to agree. I wondered if our family would enjoy it and if Darren could safely do something like that.

But everyone seemed interested so the intrigue and temptation to learn soon overpowered our doubts and before long we were owners of a .22 scoped rifle and a 12 gauge pump action shotgun. If mastering a go cart and moped were an achievement for Darren, learning to shoot would be even more so. We wondered if Darren would even be able to shoot. Could a person with severe vision problems and limited mental ability safely shoot real firearms? Were we out of our minds to let him try? Time would tell.

It turned out that the .22 rifle fitted with a telescopic scope enabled Darren to see a large fluorescent green or orange target. It was difficult for him to locate and zero in on it, but with patience and perseverance he did learn! We would always walk up to the target to examine his marksmanship, but whether or not the holes in the target were his was beside the point—he was shooting.

The 12 gauge shotgun was a different story. The first few times Darren fired it, he was kicked back at least three feet. We began to worry that he might not have enough weight and strength to handle the shotgun, but he adapted and learned how to hold the gun so that his body would absorb the kick. In fact, he began to particularly like pumping out the used shells as fast as he could—just like they did on the A Team, the boys' favorite TV show at the time. Who cared if he hit the target? The bad guys must be out there somewhere!

* * * * *

During the next few outings, we progressed, and reasonably mastered, a standing target so we decided that all of us would try to fire the 12 gauge shotgun to shoot clay pigeons, four inch round clay disc targets that are thrown out 50 to 100 feet. Everyone took his turn trying to hit the clay disc that Tom threw out with a special throwing device. Aaron shot several times ...wincing each time as the kickback of the gun slammed into his shoulder. Tom quickly found a bath towel in the van and formed a thick shoulder pad so little Aaron could continue to fire but he never did hit any targets. Maria and Andrea each took one shot and that was enough for them—almost too much. Their slight builds were no match for the heavy shotgun and the powerful kick to their shoulders. I was pretty tough and was able to hit a few discs after some practice shots. Then the old pro Darren stepped up to try his hand. He had already learned to handle the kick and loved pumping shot after shot. The big problem was that Darren could hardly see the four inch clay pigeon at arm's length—let alone at 50 to 100 feet. Always looking out for her brother, Andrea came to the rescue. She ran off to the van and came back with a big bright green Frisbee. She figured Darren would be able to see *that*. And sure enough, when Tom threw the Frisbee up in the air only a few feet in front of Darren, he *could* see it! His reaction was quick and he was fast enough to get off a shot before the Frisbee hit the ground. Now he could participate and actually hit a target! The Frisbee soon became trash but the smile on Darren's face was priceless. It turned out to be one of the many memorable family outings we look back on fondly.

On the way home from that family outing, Andrea—always the one-step-ahead child—spoke up and told us, "Because of all those school shootings, I"m a little afraid of guns…They're so dangerous."

"You should be," Tom responded. "Cars are dangerous too but that's why we all take driver's education…to be responsible and to know how to handle a car. It's necessary to understand the power of firearms and learn to follow the firearm safety rules, be responsible and always respect the damage that guns can do."

Then Tom recounted a story about when he was in school back in the 50's to illustrate his point. "I belonged to a school rifle club that shot .22 rifles at the police station gun range. My friend Randy had taken his .22 rifle to school and kept it in his locker for 2 months while he made a new gunstock for it in his woodworking class. Randy lived in the country and almost always had several .22 bullets in his pocket that he used for squirrel hunting with his buddies after school, but he was never once tempted to use that rifle in an inappropriate manner during the entire time he kept it at school. When he had finished making his new gunstock, he took it and his rifle home on the school bus. When the school bus stopped in front of his farmhouse, the bus driver asked, "Think you're a pretty good shot with that gun?"

"I think so," Randy boasted.

The driver then challenged him, "Lay that gun over the bus hood and see if you can hit that squirrel over there."

Tom added, "I realize that that could not happen now-a-days but can you see how kids back then were taught to be responsible and self-disciplined and have respect not only for firearms but for others? That's the kind of responsibility we are trying to teach you. Guns don't kill. People do. Responsible kids can drive a car and responsible kids can handle guns." And with that the mini-sermon was over and we headed for the pizza place.

* * * * *

Another activity that Tom and Darren enjoyed learning together was tae kwon do, a martial art that originated in Korea and is similar to karate in that it teaches discipline and self-defense. Aaron, being Korean, was very pleased that his big brother and dad were taking it even though his full schedule — learning and playing jazz trombone, playing baritone in the band, playing soccer and traveling with a school singing group — prevented him from participating himself. Darren loved it and became quite proficient even though each step took him twice as long to master as a normal student. He especially enjoyed non-contact sparring and breaking wooden boards with his hands and feet, and one of his favorite moves was a swift and powerful kick delivered to a heavy bag. He was able to memorize all the forms and finally ended up with a high blue belt, which was quite an achievement—the only levels above that were brown and then the prized black. Neither Tom nor Darren was able to pursue these higher levels due to injuries, but that didn't matter. With all of the physical and mental contact involved, this one-on-one time between Tom and Darren became precious, golden moments to remember.

CHAPTER 43

Challenges of the Adult World

"Now what?" we asked ourselves when at age twenty-one Darren graduated from K.B. Roberts.

There was a private, nonprofit corporation in our town that provided developmental, vocational and residential programs for adults with disabilities. At this point in Darren's life, it appeared to offer just what he needed. Under professional supervision, he would live in a group home, have a job and learn to make a life for himself. Darren's new home would only be a mile from our house so we could still see him at least a couple of times a week. It was decided and Darren began a new phase in his life.

Besides working in the workshop of the group home, Darren also had a part time job as a dishwasher at Pizza Hut and amazed everyone, including his parents, with his industry and competence. Pizza Hut seemed eager to hire Darren and other handicapped people and they were very understanding of his limited abilities. The manager often treated him to a personal pan pizza for his exceptional work. The satisfaction of being needed and having a "regular" job was far better than the pay he received. Darren needed to be needed.

For the first year or so, things went well at work and at the group home. Then came a change in staff. The first indication of trouble was when we noticed cans of beer sitting around the home. Then we learned that an evening at the bar with a houseparent was not an unusual occurrence. Trouble, indeed! If for no other reason, alcohol could seriously and dangerously interfere with any medications the residents were taking. But when we questioned the new house parents about this practice, we were informed that they had been told the residents were to be treated "normally." Apparently to the house parents—now for the most part a group of college psychology students— frequent nights out at the bar *was* "normal" but we felt it certainly wasn't the best idea in a group home of this type.

At the next parent's meeting, the new director for the six group homes was introduced. Mike was a suave, good-looking young fellow who made an impressive presentation of plans for the future of the homes, and then opened up the meeting for questions and discussion from the parents. After questions from several of the parents, I summoned up the courage to ask what I was wondering about, above all: "Are the house parents allowed to have alcohol in the group homes?"

Without a moment's hesitation, Mike shot back, "Of course, it's *their* home, too!" leaving me feeling as though my question was completely out of line.

No one pursued the matter further at that time— probably not wanting to put themselves in my awkward position—but after the meeting, several parents asked me what was behind my question.

I assured them that it wasn't without reason and shared our concerns regarding alcohol in the homes. Apparently, we were not the only concerned parents once they understood the situation. Not long after, a notice was sent out to all parents that alcohol would not be allowed in the group homes. No one offered an apology or explanation, but having that problem taken care of was well worth the embarrassment I had endured for being the one to speak out about it.

Another concern we had was the relationship between Darren and one of his housemates, Jeff, who had actually hit him several times. When we asked the staff about it, they assured us that it was just "guy stuff."

Then we learned from a former staff member who had worked at the group home workshop that more than just "guy stuff" was going on. We had heard that she had quit—or been forced to quit—over a mishandling of funds but when we spoke to her we found out that was not true. The problem was that she had been aware of a cover up of certain problems in the home and had attempted to be a whistle blower. As a result, she had been framed and forced to quit.

The cover up involved Darren and Tim, another of the residents. Apparently they were both being abused by Jeff. We were dumbfounded. How could that be? We saw Darren at least two times a week. He never so much as hinted at what was going on.

When we questioned him, he said helplessly, "I wanted to tell you. I told the staff I wanted to call you, but they said I was an adult now and needed to handle it myself."

Clearly, this was a situation beyond the control of two mentally handicapped young men. We learned that Jeff had a history of abuse to others and his presence in the home was actually a violation of one of the rules for being accepted. It stated in the application that "residents must be free of injurious behaviors to self, others and property."

It was the usual practice that the home was unstaffed from 10PM to 6AM, so the clients were on their own. However, there was a strict rule that no one could go into another's room unless invited. Not surprisingly, Jeff didn't abide by that rule. One night after the staff left, Jeff pushed his way into Darren's room. When he refused to leave,

Darren had to use the *tae kwon do* he had learned to throw him over his bed and out the door!

Another night Darren heard scuffling in Tim's room. Darren knocked on the door to see if Tim was all right.

"Go away!" came Jeff's voice from inside.

Darren knew the rule about going into another's room, of course, but he felt Tim was in trouble and needed help. When he opened the door, Jeff was on top of Tim. Darren immediately went to Tim's rescue and threw Jeff out of the room.

Darren finally told of many other such instances that had happened during the year.

Did the staff know what was going on? After a great deal of detective work and intervention from the State Attorney General's office, we found out that they *did* know. Finally, the two staff members who were responsible for not stopping the abuse were fired and put on a list that rendered them unfit to ever work with disabled clients again. But by that time, sickened by all the politics, underhandedness and cover ups on the part of the agency, we had withdrawn Darren from the program and he was again living at home.

Temporarily, this wasn't a bad situation—we loved having him home again. But how was he going to learn to make a life of his own? It would be all too easy for him to become overly dependent on us. We had seen it happen before. Harley, a mentally slow man nearing middle age, lived in our neighborhood with his mother. He was able to drive and had a responsible job, but he had never made close friends of his own. His mother was his whole life. When she died suddenly, Harley was lost. Within a year Harley himself died, overwhelmed by loneliness. We wanted Darren to build a life of his own as our other children would, so this would never happen to him.

So we set out to find another group home. This time we would be especially discriminating, profiting, we hoped, from our previous experience.

Finding a suitable group home was no easy task though and there were not that many vacancies — suitable or not. One possibility, a state-run facility we visited, was crossed off our list when we learned that working was not necessarily a part of their program. Able-bodied residents were not required to work, so they could watch TV all day or do nothing if that was their choice.

"He who doesn't work, doesn't eat," Tom paraphrased from the Bible as we made our way to the car from that visit. If a group-home administration couldn't force able people to work, then we would have to look elsewhere. Darren wouldn't mind watching TV all day should the opportunity present itself so easily, but we weren't about to let that happen. We had worked hard to instill a good work ethic in him as we had with all of our children. It was more than making money. He needed to know the feeling of fulfillment and accomplishment that can only come from working.

Finally, we learned of a Christian group-home and workshop in a town about a forty-five minute drive from our town. We were so impressed with it that we decided we could overlook any inconvenience the distance might be. And they had a vacancy!

The home was a new ranch-style brick building. Each client had his own spacious room, ten men in one wing and ten women in another with a central dining/living area in the middle. Darren was soon very happily settled in and enjoying making friends with all of the residents. The workshop was more than we could have ever hoped for. There was plenty of work and Darren was moved around so he could learn various jobs. We were pleased to see him mature and build confidence as he received satisfaction from his work.

A profile written by one of the staff offers a good picture of our young adult Darren: "Darren has a pleasant personality, treats others with respect, gets along well with everyone, is soft-spoken and cooperative, is a sharp dresser and always looks well-groomed. He is a good communicator and can carry on a good conversation and enjoys conversing with staff and friends on a one-on-one basis. Darren independently gets up in the mornings with his alarm, leaves for work on time and is punctual for meal times and activities. He comes to the med room independently to take his vitamins and minerals and is knowledgeable about them. He has wonderful leisure skills, is talented at drawing and particularly enjoys drawing space ships and dragons. In fact, one of his detailed space ship drawings is currently on display. He enjoys watching the Star Trek shows and has collected Star Trek memorabilia, is interested in tae kwon do and enjoys antique shops. Working in the workshop, Darren maintains a positive attitude, is willing to try new jobs and works hard at those jobs which are not so easy, stays on task, continues to learn new jobs and remembers these jobs well. He has a good attendance record, is at his work station on time and his pleasant personality is appreciated. Darren also has good conversation skills, a good sense of humor and is polite, caring, respectful and interested in others."

But suddenly Darren's neat little world fell apart. The state made a ruling that the residents be split up into a family setting rather than living in a dormitory-type setting with 19 other residents. In compliance, the corporation bought five homes scattered around town and divided the clients among them. Things were never the same for Darren after this upheaval. As far as he was concerned, this was a case of fixing something that wasn't broken. He had thrived on the camaraderie of dorm life. Now with only three housemates that he didn't have much in common with, he was lonely!

We decided that what Darren needed was a special friend. How about a dog? A dog is supposed to be man's best friend and wouldn't a dog be a good addition to the home, too—helping to make it more like a normal family situation?

The board didn't see it that way. No pets except goldfish or, of course, a seeing-eye dog would have to be allowed if it was necessary. Not surprisingly, Darren was not enthusiastic about getting a goldfish. What kind of friend was a goldfish? You couldn't take them for walks or watch TV and cuddle with them. So much for getting a pet to make that house a home!

Then an idea began to take form in my mind. Darren *was* legally blind, so a seeing eye dog wouldn't be out of the question, would it? In fact, a seeing eye dog could be very beneficial for him. Not long ago on an annual field trip with other residents he had had another harrowing experience of getting lost from the rest of the group because of his defective eyesight—similar to what had happened at the State Special Olympics Swim Meet. This latest experience could have had even more serious consequences. They were in a strange city walking across a parking lot toward their bus when a downpour of rain suddenly descended. Everyone took off running for the bus to get out of the rain. Everyone except Darren that is. He hadn't been able to see which way they had gone! When you can see only a few feet ahead, it doesn't take much to lose your bearings. He had stood helplessly in the pouring rain wondering what to do and where to go. Fortunately, someone had discovered he was missing and came looking for him.

Didn't incidents like that—and the likelihood of them occurring again—indicate that Darren's eyesight *was* bad enough to warrant a seeing eye dog? But where do you get one? And how? We asked around and heard of an organization called Pilot Dogs in Columbus, Ohio. As with many other guide dog training organizations, we found that the Lion's Club funded most, if not all, of the cost of training and placement. That cost would be around

$5500…but the cost to *us* would be absolutely *free*. What a blessing!

Both an ophthalmologist and an optometrist examined Darren's vision. There was no question that his eyesight was bad enough. The detail that a person with normal eyesight sees at 700 feet is the detail that Darren sees at 20 feet away and his eyesight could vary as much as 700/20 to 200/20.

This, in hindsight, no doubt explained why Darren misbehaved so much when he was little. We remembered a family outing to the circus when he was about five years old. Andrea wanted to sit high in the bleachers so we did, and we couldn't understand why Darren was so wiggly and wild. We almost offered him to the circus as a wild monkey that looked like a kid! Now it all fit…he hadn't been able to *see* all the wonderful things going on way down there in the rings. And to compound the problem, we had bought him a big cotton candy which — being pure sugar — didn't do a thing towards calming him down.

Be that as it may, the ophthalmologist at this examination told us that his eyes were so bad that nothing could be done and they could get worse. Not a happy prospect — but it *did* mean that Darren qualified for a seeing eye dog!

So we filled out the five page application and sent it — along with the doctor's report — to Pilot Dogs in Ohio and then settled in for a long wait.

At last came a call from the director of Pilot Dogs. Darren had been accepted, but with some reservations. They wondered if Darren — being retarded — would be able to give a dog the care and consistent commands that were necessary? For one thing, the dog must be walked one to two miles a day, rain or shine. Also, in a group home situation, there might be too much confusion for a seeing eye dog — too many "bosses." However, Pilot Dogs was willing to give him a try.

Darren would fly—alone—to Ohio, work day and night training with the dog for one month, then fly back with the dog...*if* he passed the test.

Pilot Dogs made all the flying arrangements, but sending Darren off on the plane all by himself was more daunting for us than we could ever have imagined. As soon as we arrived at the airport, we confirmed his flight and told them that he was legally blind and mentally handicapped, so he must have assistance changing planes in St. Louis.

We were assured that this would be arranged. There would be no need to check in again when we got upstairs—everything was taken care of.

But once upstairs in the waiting room, we began to feel even more nervous. I suggested that maybe we should check to see that everything was all right with the ticket.

The man at the counter obligingly looked over the ticket. Yes, everything was in order.

"And someone will take him to his connecting flight in St. Louis?" I pressed further.

Well no, he didn't see anything about that—but he then made the necessary arrangements.

What could have happened if we hadn't checked? Now it was even harder to be calm. How many *other* things could go wrong? Shakily, we prayed with Darren and then watched him walk onto the plane all by himself...off to Ohio on a new adventure under the care of people we had never even met. Would they keep him on his special diet of no sugar and give him the nutritional supplements that had been keeping him healthy? Would he be able to handle the rigorous training? Tears welled up in my eyes. I had wanted a dog for Darren so badly and I had worked hard to get this far—but now I was overcome by fear.

We prayed again as the plane took off. Darren was in God's hands now and that was that.

We called several times a week to see how Darren was doing. His dog was a yellow lab, already named—for whatever reason—Stix. And interestingly enough, it was Stix who chose Darren, not the other way around, when the dogs and people were paired early on, and that seemed to please Darren.

The trainer was guarded with his comments. Darren was doing all right, but he lacked self-confidence. For one thing, Darren wasn't sure he could rely on his own hearing to tell when cars were coming when crossing streets. In reality, the dog depends on the owner's commands—the dog is not so much in control as it might appear to a casual observer. The trainer felt sure that Darren could do it, if only *he* believed it. We prayed constantly that Darren would understand what he had to do and be able to bring home the dog.

Meanwhile change was brewing at home with us. Tom had just retired from his job and we were making plans to relocate. We took the time while Darren was gone to look for a home in a little warmer climate and after a great deal of thought and especially prayer, we had settled on what looked like a promising location, as central as possible, considering that our other three children were somewhat scattered. Andrea—having finished college with honors—had a good job in the northern part of the state; Maria was married with two little ones, Mason and Gabryel and would be traveling with her military husband, Keane; and Aaron was attending a Christian college in the South.

The day before Darren was scheduled to come home, the trainer still had reservations. However, when we explained that Darren would not be going back to the group home, but would be relocating with us and would have our guidance and encouragement with the dog, the trainer decided in the affirmative.

What a thrill the next day to see Darren walk off the plane with his dog. Literally aglow, he seemed a littler taller and more mature. He had made it! And handsome Stix seemed proud and pleased, too.

By not giving up, being persistent, having faith — and by the Grace of God — Darren had just crossed another Red Sea.

CHAPTER 44

The Special Force

We couldn't have put into words exactly why we were moving, or why we had chosen that locale, but we had felt that God's hand was in it. However, after looking at some seventy houses during three trips that each lasted three days while Darren was in Ohio, we were beginning to wonder. Nothing was quite right. As we neared the end of the list on the third trip we said, "God, if you want us to stay where we are, that's all right. If we don't find a house by Wednesday, we"ll know that we're to stay put."

Late Wednesday afternoon we were driving through a wooded area with the realtor when we came to a plain little house below the road, almost buried among the trees. It could have been mistaken for a mobile home and looked like it might fall off the hill if given a little push. The yard, quite frankly, was rather junky looking—filled with metal sculptures, some seemingly in progress.

"You don't want to look at this one, do you?" the realtor asked skeptically.

Well, yes…as long as we were already here…

What we thought was the front door was actually the back door so we walked into the kitchen. And what a surprise awaited us! Beyond the dining room were sliding glass doors that opened onto a deck with a magnificent view of a beautiful wooded valley and a charming pond with more of the same glorious beauty visible through the four vaulted floor-to-ceiling windows gracing the spacious living room. The realtor mentioned that there was a total of *six* acres!

We looked at each other in silent agreement and just *knew*, "This is it!" Never mind the worn carpet and the need for a general sprucing up. We preferred our unique style anyway so we would enjoy redecorating it to our own tastes.

We made an offer that night, contingent on our house being sold. Two months later, our house in Baldwin was ready to be put on the market and in just two days, we had three people interested in buying it.

We decided it would be safe to take the contingency off the new house. And it was a good thing that we did! While the owner of the house was answering our realtor's call in the bedroom to inform him of this, another prospective buyer was waiting in the living room ready to make an offer.

"Sorry, the house just sold!" the owner told him after talking with our realtor.

After we learned about this close call, we were sure that God wanted that house for us. We didn't know why, but we put our trust in Him and knew that we would find out in good time.

A week later, with two U-Haul truck loads and a trailer—Tom, Darren, Stix and I—moved into our "little cabin in the woods." Aaron got permission to take a few days off from the Christian Camp counselor summer job he had taken during college break. Thanks to Aaron and the two friends he enlisted, the move went very smoothly and we were very grateful for their help!

* * * * *

Before considering this move, we had talked with the Regional Center for Developmental Disabilities regarding a suitable group home and work program for Darren. We were assured there would be no problem, but by the time we finally got situated in our new home things didn't look as rosy as we had been led to believe. It seems there were State budget and other problems.

So for about a year, Darren was stuck at home with Mom and Dad. Naturally we loved having him with us, but it was a bit dull for him with no young people around after he had gotten used to the activity and camaraderie of a group home. It was a good thing he had Stix to keep him company.

And fortunately, we discovered Sporting Chance. This organization was started by a man who had worked with Special Olympics and felt there needed to be a sports league that would give *any* player—regardless of his ability or handicap—"a sporting chance" to participate in sports including basketball games. The emphasis was not on winning, but just on having fun playing the game.

In basketball games, the better players who understood the rules and were able to follow them accepted the lesser skilled players. True sportsmanship! For example, Darren had trouble seeing the ball, especially when it was passed to him too fast, but he was fair at dribbling and passing and would sometimes get rebounds that happened to come his way. During his first few games at Sporting Chance, he hesitantly shuffled his way down the court. But his confidence increased as he became familiar with his surroundings, grew confident that he would not run into a wall and realized no one was going to make fun of him. As a result, his hesitant shuffling gradually transformed into running with long assured strides. So here was a legally blind player not only thoroughly enjoying the game but actually doing well—even scoring an occasional basket!

The referees knew each player's specific skills and abilities and called fouls and rule infractions accordingly. If a player was a good dribbler and understood the double dribble rule, the referee would call them on the double dribble. On the other hand, a player who did not understand basic dribbling would not be called.

One potential player sat in the bleachers with his parents for three nights in a row and could not be coaxed into taking part in the game, though the referees actually went into the bleachers to try to persuade him to take part. Finally he followed a referee onto the floor. When the referee handed him the ball at one end of the court, he tucked the ball under his arm like a football fullback, charged without dribbling to the other end of the court and tried to throw the ball into the basket. The shot missed even the backboard, but everyone was overjoyed that he had tried and applauded loudly and enthusiastically. After that, he played a little in every game!

As a spectator sport, a Sporting Chance game was great fun. We would find ourselves identifying with all the players — whether on the court or on the bench. Most spectators cheered for both sides — clapping, cheering and whistling when *any* player participated in the game in any way — even if it was only throwing the ball into play. As to the score — who cared? What mattered was the joy of participation.

"Let nothing be done through selfish ambition or conceit but in lowliness of mind let each esteem others better than himself" Philippians 2:3 (NKJ).

Shortly after moving into our new neighborhood we found a nearby church that we all enjoyed. One Sunday after the service, everyone was invited to a pizza lunch. We arrived a little late and all the tables appeared to be filled. A man stood up and motioned for us to join his family, which we did. In the course of conversation, we discovered that he was a pastor who worked with a group called Special Touch, a nationwide organization that provides spiritual programs, socialization and prayer for people with all kinds of handicaps. When we told him that we had been searching for a group home for Darren, he suggested Special Force Family Ministries. We had noticed that name printed on a van at a Sporting Chance event and it had peeked our curiosity — but afterward we couldn't remember anything but the "Force" part of the name. When we tried to quiz our social worker, he had not been able to recall an organization with that word in its name, so we had come to a dead end and it had slipped our minds for the time being. Now, thanks to God's careful planning, here we were getting all the information on it from this kind pastor!

What a blessing! The Special Force Group Home turned out to be just what we had been praying for! And no wonder...the "Special Force" the name refers to is God!

The next thing we knew, Darren and Stix were happily situated at Special Force with thirteen other men with varying degrees of handicaps from slightly autistic to very high functioning.

This group home runs like a well-oiled machine, even though there is constant coming and going due to the various activities and work schedules. Everyone has chores to do and is responsible for his own laundry and for cleaning his room. When disagreements arise, the residents respond with love and respect, so most of the time they are able to work out problems on their own. Darren is content and quite happy to call this his home, and a steady part time job at the nearby Steak 'n' Shake Restaurant makes his life even more fulfilling.

So we now know the reason behind our latest move to the cabin in the woods. Thank goodness we trusted in God, The Special Force, and followed His lead — even when we had no idea why, or what, the result would be!

We were reminded of God's words in 2 Corinthians 12:9: "...My grace is sufficient for you, for power is perfected in weakness." (NAS)

What Good Am I?

Some time after Darren had moved into the Special Force Group Home, he and Stix went with us to visit Maria and Keane and their little family at Fort Polk, Louisiana, where Keane was stationed as an army mechanic. We had taken our van because it was roomy enough for Stix, and now we were on our way home. Stix and Darren were in their usual place in the back.

There was plenty of time for conversation and somehow the subject of death came up. In particular, what if we—Darren's parents—died?

"Does that worry you, Darren?" I asked.

"Yeah!" he answered, sounding very worried. "Then what happens to me? I won't have anyone—except Stix. Maybe I won't even have him…" His voice trailed off.

"Well, you"ll still have Andrea and Maria and Aaron, you know. They"ll always be your family."

"Yeah, but they all live a long way away. And they all have their own families and homes to look after. Andrea has Doug and Riley and she's a successful marketing director for a large hospital in Iowa. Maria has her kids—Mason and Gabryel—and gets to live in Germany because Keane is in the Army. Aaron graduated from college and is managing people in a bank. He bought a new car and has his own apartment where you can see Pensacola Bay. And someday he will have his own family—but I won't have anyone..." As he spoke, Darren's voice was quieter, his words came out slower and at the end of the sentence his thoughts drifted off into hopelessness. The reality of his future had just gripped him...possibly for the first time.

We knew that Darren had made our family "different," but we doubted he had surmised that fact. He taught our entire family lessons about caring, loving, focusing on helping others, appreciating and using the abilities we have, and that the love of others—not ourselves—leads to a joyful and peaceful mind and success and fulfillment. We knew what Darren had done for us, but what could we say to comfort him? What could bring success and fulfillment for Darren? What could bring joy into Darren's life?

We drove in silence for a few minutes, captivated by a moment of soul searching. Yes, this *was* Darren's reality—whether we liked it or not. What could we say?

Darren finally broke the silence with some other serious questions. First he wanted to know where grandpa Balcer—who had just recently died—was now. Is he still alive somewhere? Is he with God? Then he asked about us. When we died where would we go? And that led him to thinking about himself. Someday he would die also. Would *he* be with God?

It was not that Darren didn't know the answer to these questions. This was not the first time we had talked about heaven and eternity. He had heard the gospel message all his life. He knew about the love of God that sent Jesus to be the Savior of a wicked and undeserving world. But now we wondered if he had ever applied it to himself personally?

We *thought* he had when he was a young boy, but apparently while growing up Darren had wandered away. The years in the earlier group homes had been down times spiritually, until eventually church and God were not an important part of his life. Although he attended services, we realized now that was probably more or less to please us. For some time it had seemed that he saw no reason to listen or even stay awake. We had become more and more concerned about Darren's spirit. What had become of the little boy who had chosen to make God his "boss"? Although he never put it into words, it had become quite evident over time that pleasing himself was of the utmost importance. It seemed that his real concern these days was what was in it for Darren?

"What good am I?" Darren finally asked rhetorically. It was more of a statement than a question to be answered because Darren well knew his limitations. They had always been a part of his life and to him they far outweighed anything he would have to be proud of. As far as he was concerned, the pluses in his life at this point were not even worth considering. If self-pride, self-esteem is as important to a successful and happy life as it is generally thought to be—even in some Christian circles—Darren was in trouble.

"Doesn't God love Andrea...and Maria...and Aaron more than me?" Again, the question was more of a statement. It was obvious to Darren that his sisters and brother must be the more favored ones. They weren't handicapped. They had everything going for them.

Sadly, Darren thought he had it all figured out. He felt that God loved them more. Don't good things happen to good people—those that God loves best—and bad things... well...

Then I remembered that this was the conclusion Jesus' disciples had come to regarding a man who had been born blind.

Here we were with the same question we had encountered that long ago Sunday morning when we had rescued the church nursery attendants from our out-of-sorts toddler. "They seem like such nice people," we had overheard one of the ladies muse as we went out the door. Whether she added, "but of course they can't be, with a child like that," we didn't hear, but that was what her tone implied.

Fresh in our minds was the day's sermon from the ninth chapter of John about the man who had been born blind. "Who did sin," the disciples asked, "this man or his parents, that he was born blind?" *Surely, somebody must have done something bad to cause this tragedy*, they thought.

What did Jesus tell them? It was that the works of God might be seen! That God might be glorified! What did it take to show how wonderful God is? A poor blind man that nobody wanted to be bothered with. This is TO SHOW THE WORKS OF GOD! What looked like a bad thing, was not that at all! God made it into something good.

What we think is defective is not defective at all. It is God's plan to use us for His glory. We need to be willing to surrender our lives to and for Him. Nothing happens in a Christian's life that hasn't passed through the mind of God first.

"All things work together for good to them that love God, to them that are called according to his purpose," Romans 8:28 declares. We may not know WHY bad things happen, but we know that God can bring good from them. God can be glorified through them.

We had seen that happen in our family over and over, we reminded Darren. Think of all the people who have been helped because of what we learned searching for answers to your problems. And Aaron. Where would Aaron be today if it weren't for you? And Maria? Where would she be? You, Darren, have a ministry in just being yourself.

Maybe we get in God's way and keep Him from doing the good that He wants to do in our lives and in the world when we think we are capable of being a blessing to the world all by ourselves? Hmmmmm. Scripture points out "The person who wishes to boast should boast only of what the Lord has done." I Corinthians 1:30-32 (NLT) Can it be that self-esteem is not as important as some have thought?

Could it even be a hindrance to God's working, to His being glorified? Jesus thought so. What did He say about "self?" "If any man will come after me, let him deny himself, and take up his cross daily, and follow me." Luke 9:23 (KJV) "Deny himself!" "Follow Me!"

"What is life all about?" We remembered that question on the card in the Ungame we used to play.

"It's LOVE!" eight-year-old Darren had answered first off without even having to think about it. How right he was!

LOVE! If a person doesn't have love, he is nothing, no matter what anybody thinks. The Bible says that very clearly in I Corinthians 13, and then goes on to paint a portrait of what love, God's kind of love, looks like in action. Nowhere in the picture is there anything about looking out for self. *"Love…does not envy. . . does not boast… is not proud…is not rude…is not self-seeking."*

It's getting self out of the way — *denying* self — and letting God's love come through.

"Love is patient…kind…not easily angered…keeps no record of wrongs…does not delight in evil but rejoices with the truth…always protects, always trusts, always hopes, always perseveres."

But more than that Darren began to realize: It's Christ Himself living out His life in every child of His who chooses to deny self and follow Him. *"For me, to live is Christ – His life in me…"* Philippians 1:21 (AMP)

As we were heading along the highway toward home, we prayed together. For Darren it was a coming back after being away for too long. For all of us it was a quiet time of drawing close to God with praise and thankfulness to Him.

"What good am I?" is no longer important. Darren is coming to realize that, like everybody else, his worth is in being a child of God. As a child of God the goodness, the love and the glory of God is reflected from within him. We praise the Lord for the wonderful blessing Darren has been to our family and others.

"I will praise You, for I am fearfully and wonderfully made; marvelous are Your works, and that my soul knows very well." Psalm 139:14 (NKJ)

To order additional copies of
The Little Boy That Could

please visit our website:

www.TheLittleBoyThatCouldBook.com

For your enjoyment, we have posted a
collection of family photos on our site that
correspond with the stories in our book and
illustrate many of the memorable
moments of our lives!

As a courtesy, we have also included a
section on the nutritional supplements that
played an important role in helping us to
overcome many of the health challenges we
faced, both with our son and as a family.

GOD BLESS!

"All Your works shall praise You, O Lord."
Psalm 145:10

TO ORDER

The Little Boy That Could

FOR RESALE

PLEASE CONTACT:

UNITED WRITERS PRESS, INC.
P.O. BOX 326
TUCKER, GEORGIA 30085-0326

TOLL-FREE
866-857-4678

ATLANTA AREA
770-925-4678

WWW.UNITEDWRITERSPRESS.COM